NATURE
ON YOUR DOORSTEP

BLACK CAT

Contents

WILDLIFE IN TOWNS
by Graham Carter

Town and country	4
Exploring a park	6
Trees	8
Wasteland	10
Flowers of the wasteland	12
Small mammals	14
The roadside	16
Insects and other tiny animals	18
Along the canal	20
Life in the water	22
Birds	24
Inside a house	26
Who lives in your house?	28

LIFE IN PONDS AND STREAMS by Oliver Aston

Looking at ponds	30
From mountains to the sea	31
A mountain stream	32
Waterbirds	34
A river	36
Fishes	38
Water plants	40
Insects and other tiny animals	42
A river bank	44
Plants on the bank	46
Animals that live near water	48
A pond	50
Tiny animals in the water	52
Pollution	54

LIFE ON THE SEASHORE
by David Gilman

Sandy shores	56
Starfish, sea-urchins, sea anemones	58
Worms and jellyfishes	60
A rock pool	62
Molluscs	64
The crab family	66
Sand dunes	68
Beach plants	70
Shore birds	72
Cliffs	74
Cliff birds	76
Coastal plants	78
A salt-marsh	80

THE WILDLIFE OF WOODLANDS
by John Waters

Leaf or needle?	82
Our varied woodlands	83
Looking up in a broad-leaved woodland	84
Trees of broad-leaved woodland	86
On the ground in broad-leaved woodland	88
Wild flowers	90
Mammals	92
Birds	94
Looking up in a coniferous woodland	96
Trees of coniferous woodland	98
On the ground in coniferous woodland	100
Insects and other tiny animals	102
Plants without flowers	104
The web of life	106

THE WILDLIFE OF FARMLAND by David Gilman

A meadow	108
Larger animals	110
A hedgerow	112
Birds	114
Tiny animals	116
A cornfield, by day and night	118
Plant pests and diseases	120
Animal pests and diseases	122
A farmyard	124
Wild flowers	126
Chalk downs	128
Farm animals	130
Farm crops	132

THE WILDLIFE OF MOUNTAINS AND MOORLANDS
by Penny Anderson

A mountain	134
Birds	136
Moorland	138
Trees and shrubs	140
Butterflies and moths	142
Flowering plants	144
Heathland	146
Large animals	148
A bog	150
Non-flowering plants	152
Grasslands	154
Tiny animals	156
Using the land	158

Acknowledgments   160

Town and country

We all know the difference between towns and the countryside. Towns contain buildings, roads and railways. The countryside is open space, with few buildings. This may give us the wrong idea about the wildlife in each.

Natural or artificial?

Many people think that town habitats are all man-made, while habitats in the countryside are natural. This is not true. Almost all the countryside in Europe has been shaped by people. The natural land cover in most European countries is woodland. Over the past few hundred years, most of the trees have been cut down. Apart from mountain tops and the seashore, countryside habitats are as unnatural as those in towns.

Some city habitats may even be more 'natural' than the surrounding countryside. Every town has some areas of wasteland. This is land which has never been built on. Wasteland is often found beside railway sidings, inside factory fences or between blocks of buildings. Almost all the plants there have grown from seeds which were brought in by natural means, such as the wind, birds and animals. The land has not been treated with weedkillers or fertilizers. The result is a 'natural' community of plants and animals.

'Nothing lives in a town.'

Another common mistake is to believe that country habitats are rich in different species of plants and animals, while town habitats are not. In fact, many areas of the countryside are almost empty. For example, thousands of hectares of woodland have been planted with North American trees. Very few European animals can live there.

In contrast to these barren landscapes, many city habitats are very rich in species. A typical garden contains dozens of different plants, including shrubs and trees. These, in turn, provide food for hundreds of different invertebrates.

Similar habitats

Some areas of towns have many similarities to parts of the countryside. Roads, walls and roofs are like the bare rock of mountains and sea cliffs, and there is very little soil in which plants can take root. Many buildings have wide ledges, like the rock ledges on sea cliffs.

The animals and plants which live in the centre of cities are often ones that live on cliffs and mountains. Lichens and mosses grow on rooftops. Pigeons nest on the stone ledges on buildings. They are descended from rock doves, which live on rocky sea cliffs.

▼ People in towns like to visit open green spaces. Parks imitate the countryside's water, grass and woodland, and provide a variety of different habitats.

◄ Ledges on buildings are like those on sea-cliffs. Birds, such as starlings, use them as nesting and roosting sites. Thousands may roost on one building.

► Bats normally shelter in caves or hollow trees during the day and come out at night to hunt. In town centres many bats roost in towers and large buildings instead.

Some parts of the town, such as parks, are designed to be like countryside. Lawns represent pastureland, groves of trees imitate woodland, and shrubberies resemble the scrub which is often found at the edge of woodland. This variety of habitats attracts many animals.

Town habitats

Some habitats are only found in towns. Derelict land is land which has been used in the past, but is now lying idle, such as sites where buildings once stood.

Even if these derelict sites only lie idle for a few years before they are built on once again, they provide very important living spaces for city wildlife. Native plants like thistles, willowherb and grasses are very common. They hide the ugliness of derelict land and provide food for insects, which in turn are eaten by birds.

Another city habitat is the refuse tip. All the waste materials from houses, restaurants and food shops are food for birds and animals which scavenge on these tips, such as rats, gulls and crows. The rotting waste produces heat, so some insects which like warmth live here, such as cockroaches and house crickets.

Tips are also exciting places to look for plants. The refuse includes seeds of many kinds, such as seed from birdcages and spices from restaurants. These may germinate in the warmth so that plants from all over the world grow and flower on the rubbish.

Other habitats which are more common in towns than in the countryside include houses and other heated buildings and, of course, people. These all provide food and shelter for many different animals and plants.

How animals and plants arrive

Town habitats are colonized very quickly by animals and plants from the surrounding countryside. Many birds, insects and seeds fly in or are carried by the wind. Some come by water. They may drift down to the town from the upper reaches of a river. Others reach the dockland areas as accidental passengers in cargo ships.

Motorway verges, canal banks and railway embankments form green highways reaching from the heart of the country right into the city centre. These routes are followed by many of the larger animals. Foxes, in particular, travel by such routes.

This book looks at some town habitats and shows you many of the plants and animals living there. As you will see, studying wildlife in towns can be fascinating.

◄ Public and private gardens often contain rockeries. These copy the conditions on a mountain, where there is little soil and water drains away quickly.

► Artificial ponds and streams are very important nature reserves. Many natural pools in the countryside are disappearing as farmland is drained.

Exploring a park

Although they are artificial, parks can look very natural. They often contain several different countryside habitats, such as grassland, woodland and ponds.

▼ Honey bees

Honey bees are common visitors to flowers in parks. They start life as eggs, which are laid inside six-sided wax cells (**1**). The eggs hatch into larvae, which are fed on nectar and pollen collected from flowers (**2**). Some of the cells are used to store food for the winter (**3**).

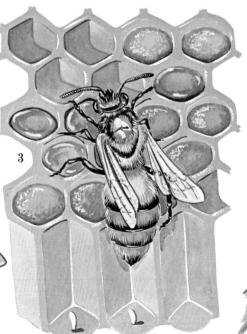

▼ Froghopper

The nymphs suck sap from plant stems, and live inside a protective covering of foam, often called cuckoo spit. The adults (**right**) jump into the air when disturbed.

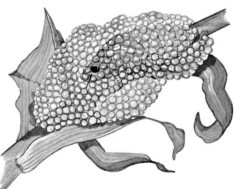

▼ Eyed hawkmoth
Willows are often planted beside lakes. Their leaves are eaten by eyed hawkmoth caterpillars. The adult shows pink hindwings with bright blue eyespots to frighten predators.

Key
1 Ash
2 Horse chestnut
3 Cedar of Lebanon
4 Crow
5 Fallow deer
6 Weeping willow
7 Herring gull
8 Magnolia
9 Maple
10 Oak
11 Black-headed gull
12 Teal
13 Coot
14 Male fern
15 Laurel
16 Viburnum
17 Berberis
18 Rabbit
19 Dabchick
20 Mute swan
21 Shelduck
22 Starling
23 Common shrew
24 Wren
25 Thrush
26 Fairy-ring toadstools
27 Hedge sparrow
28 Nuthatch
29 Squirrel
30 Hover-flies
31 Brimstone butterfly
32 Small copper butterfly
33 Common vole

The flowers in parks attract many **insects**, including butterflies (31, 32) and hover-flies (30). **Birds** come to feed on the insects. You may see nuthatches (28) and jays as well as starlings (22), thrushes (25) and crows (4). Most parks have squirrels. Some also have deer.

▶ Mandarin duck
Ducks and other waterfowl are often introduced to lakes. One of the most attractive introduced species is the mandarin duck, originally from China and Japan. It is now widely bred in Europe, and normally nests in trees.

7

Trees

Trees are an important part of the city landscape. They give food and shelter to a variety of insects, and birds nest in them. Many have beautiful flowers or fruit, which add colour to the street.

*Not to scale. The maximum height is given.

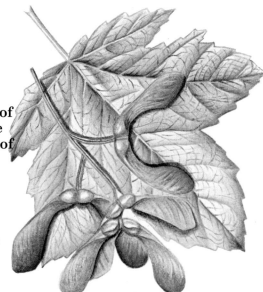

▲**Sycamore** 30m
A large, spreading tree, often planted in parks. It also grows easily and quickly wherever the winged fruits land. In early summer it has small flowers.

▼**Silver birch** 30m
A graceful tree with silvery bark. Catkins appear in early summer and are followed by winged seeds. Many moth caterpillars eat the leaves.

▲**Common or pedunculate oak** 45m
A large, deciduous tree with spreading branches and a huge trunk. It has acorns on long stalks in autumn, and is often found in parks.

▲**Rowan, Mountain ash** 20m
This beautiful tree is said to bring good luck if planted in a garden. It has orange berries which blackbirds and thrushes eat in winter, and will grow well in poor soil.

▼**Robinia, Locust, False acacia** 30m
Sweet-scented white flowers produce long seed-pods, which often stay throughout winter.

▼**Catalpa, Indian bean tree** 15m
From North America. Large sprays of spotted flowers appear in late summer and produce thin seed pods, which can be 35cm long.

▲**Beech** 40m
Beech leaves grow so thickly that they cut out light, preventing other plants growing underneath the tree. It has hard triangular nuts in prickly cases, which split when ripe.

▲**Ash** 40m
A tall tree with smooth grey bark and black winter buds. There are several attractive varieties, including the weeping ash. The fruits each have a wing, and are called *keys*.

▲Maidenhair tree, Gingko 30m
A very old Chinese tree, whose fossil remains have been found in rocks which are millions of years old. Its fan-shaped leaves have no central rib.

▲Whitebeam 20m
This is often planted as a decorative tree. Its leaves have white undersides, which show when the wind blows. In autumn it has orange-red berries.

▲Hornbeam 30m
A small tree or shrub with smooth grey bark, often planted in small open spaces. Its tiny green flowers produce hard nuts, each surrounded by a three-lobed wing.

▼ Scots pine 35m
This tree is often planted in parks and gardens. It has scaly, reddish bark and short blue-green needles, which grow in pairs.

▼ Corsican pine 35m
Another common ornamental evergreen tree. Its needles are up to 15cm long and grow in pairs. This tree originally came from Southern Europe.

▲Cedar of Lebanon 40m
A large, spreading tree, often found in parks. Short dark-green needles grow in upright clusters, and it has tight, barrel-shaped cones.

▲Metasequoia, Dawn redwood 19m
Thought to be extinct, this evergreen was re-discovered in China in 1945. It can now be found growing in many city parks.

Tree shapes

In winter you can identify trees by their shapes.

Horse chestnut   Oak   Norway spruce   Ash

Every tree grows in a different way. Branches may be straight or twisted, drooping or upright. The outline of the tree may be wide and spreading or thin and compact.

These are some common trees in winter.

Waste-land

Waste and derelict land are very valuable nature reserves in most towns and cities. Plants and animals can live there almost unaffected by people. The grass is not mown and shrubs are not pruned. Plants are not destroyed by weedkillers and insecticides are not used. Animals can breed and raise their young without being disturbed.

▼ A **black redstart** (1) sings from a broken gutter. This handsome bird nests in holes in walls and usually eats insects

▲ Caterpillars

Nettles are eaten by many caterpillars. This is the caterpillar of the peacock butterfly, which is often found in groups. Red admiral and small tortoiseshell butterflies also lay their eggs on nettles.

▼ Mosquitoes and midges

The common gnat (**1**) breeds in any still water. The eggs hatch into larvae (**2**), which feed head-down in the water, taking in air through a tube. The pupa (**3**) hangs just below the surface. The adult female feeds on the blood of birds. On the right is a midge.

Key

1 Redstart	13 Dead nettle
2 Nettles	14 Lupin
3 Sowthistle	15 Wren
4 Herring gull	16 Starlings
5 Oxford ragwort	17 Opium poppy
6 Crows	18 Ragwort
7 Rowan	19 False oat grass
8 Silver birch	20 Soft brome
9 Kestrel	21 Brambles
10 Hawthorn	22 Yorkshire fog
11 Badger sett	23 Scentless mayweed
12 Buddleia	24 Rosebay willowherb

▶ A **kestrel** (9) hovers over the railway embankment, looking for mice or voles. It nests on the ledges of large buildings.

▼ **Butterflies**
Buddleia (12) attracts many insects, particularly butterflies. The red admiral may have migrated from southern Europe. Small tortoiseshells spend the winter here.

Red admiral butterfly

Small tortoiseshell butterfly

▼ **Elephant hawkmoth caterpillar on rosebay willowherb (24)**
The 'eyes' of the caterpillar are not real, but just protective colouring. The adult moths fly at night, hovering while they drink nectar from flowers.

A rich variety of **plants** grows on undisturbed wasteland, and provides food for many different animals. The first plants to arrive often include shepherd's purse, groundsel, fat-hen, annual meadow grass, knotgrass and chickweed. They cover the soil quickly, then slower-growing plants can take root. Scentless mayweed (23) and ragwort (18) mingle with pink rosebay willowherb (24) and even, occasionally, a purple opium poppy (17). More permanent grasses arrive, such as soft brome (20), false oat grass (19) and Yorkshire fog (22).

Insects and birds feed on the plants. Small trees, like rowan (7), silver birch (8) and hawthorn (10), grow on embankments. Under them mice, voles and rabbits find shelter, and badgers may dig their setts (11).

11

Flowers
of the wasteland

An interesting mixture of plants grows on wasteland. Some are common in the countryside, others have escaped from gardens. *Not to scale. Average height given.

◀**Chickweed** 5–40cm
This tiny trailing plant is a very common annual. It grows quickly on bare soil in parks, gardens and on wasteland.

▶**Honesty** 30–100cm
Originally a garden plant. In early summer it has purple or white flowers. The silvery flat seed pods are often used for decoration.

▶**Knotgrass** 30cm when upright
This annual is often one of the first plants to colonize waste ground or bare soil in gardens. It usually trails along the ground.

◀**Sorrel** 10–100cm
The green flower spikes appear in early summer, then change to red. The leaves have a lemony taste and can be added to salads.

◀**Rosebay willowherb, Fireweed** 30–120cm
Often found in large clumps, with tall spires of pink flowers or fluffy seeds. One of the first plants to grow after a fire.

▶**Large bindweed** 1–3m
The trumpet-shaped flowers each last for only one day. It spreads by long, creeping underground stems, which are very difficult to dig out.

▶**Fat-hen** 30–90cm
A common weed of gardens, fat-hen will also colonize disturbed ground on derelict sites. Its green flower spikes grow in summer. The mealy green leaves used to be eaten as a vegetable.

◀**Shepherd's purse** 3–40cm
A common plant which has tiny white flowers throughout the year. Its heart-shaped seedpods look like the purses once carried by shepherds. They split when ripe.

◀**Ivy-leaved toadflax** 60cm
A dainty little trailing plant with lilac and yellow flowers in summer. Its leaves look like those of ivy. It was originally grown in gardens, but is now found on many walls.

▶ **Ribwort plantain** 40cm
A perennial weed of lawns and roadside verges. The leaves grow in a flat rosette. In summer tall stalks grow from the centre with spikes of tiny brownish flowers.

▶ **Creeping buttercup** 15cm
This pretty plant flowers throughout the summer. It is a troublesome weed in gardens, because it spreads so well. It sends out runners from which new plants grow.

◀ **Common ragwort** 30-150cm
This common plant has many bright yellow flower-heads on branched stems. It is eaten by the black and orange striped caterpillars of the cinnabar moth.

◀ **Goldenrod** 60–250cm
This is a garden plant which often escapes to wasteland. It has tiny yellow flowers which grow in clusters, and long thin leaves. It spreads by underground stems.

▶ **Spear thistle** 50–150cm
This tall prickly plant with sharp toothed leaves is common on wasteland and by roads. The flower-heads produce fluffy seeds which blow away in autumn or are eaten by goldfinches.

▶ **Michaelmas daisy** 40–120cm
An old-fashioned garden plant which grows in clumps. In autumn it has clusters of sweet-scented flowers, which attract small tortoiseshell butterflies.

◀ **Red dead-nettle** 15-30cm
This is a common plant on wasteland and often grows in gardens. It is not a nettle and does not sting. It has square stems, and flowers from early summer to autumn.

◀ **Honeysuckle** 6m
This sweetly-scented climber often grows on undisturbed derelict land. Moths feed on the flowers at night. In autumn it has red berries.

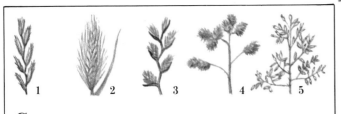

Grasses
The commonest wild flowers in towns are rarely noticed. These are the grasses, which grow everywhere.
    The five above are often found.
1 Couch 150cm **2** Wild barley 50cm
3 Perennial rye 50cm **4** Cock's-foot 100cm
5 Yorkshire fog 100cm

▶ **Bird's foot trefoil** 10-40cm
This attractive little trailing plant grows on wasteland and as a weed in lawns. The flowers are yellow, with red tips, and grow in clusters. In autumn they become long seedpods which look like birds' feet. It has many different names, for example *Bacon and eggs* and *Lady's slipper*.

Small mammals

Although many different mammals live in towns, they are not often seen. This is because most of them are *nocturnal* (active at night). Squirrels are an exception, and can be seen throughout the day. Others, like rabbits and hedgehogs, may be seen in the evening or early morning.

*Not to scale. The size given is the body-length of an adult including tail.

How a bat finds food

▲ Bats feed on small flying insects, such as moths. They use a special method to find them. As a bat flies it squeaks all the time.

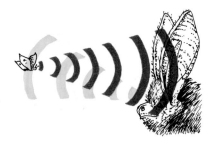

▲ If these sounds hit an insect, some of them are reflected back to the bat. It follows the echoes to the insect.

▼ **Shrew** 90–120mm
This tiny mammal feeds on slugs, worms and insects. It has a very large appetite and often hunts during the day. The shrew has poor eyesight, but a keen sense of smell. It can be distinguished from mice and voles by its very pointed nose and dark brown fur.

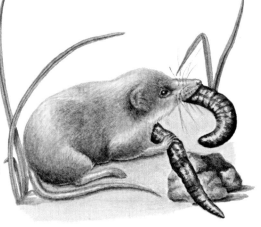

▼ **Long-tailed field mouse** 150–225mm
A common garden animal, the field mouse often makes its home in a garden shed, and will sometimes come into a house in winter. It feeds on plants and seeds.

▼ **House mouse** 140–180mm
This mouse lives in walls and under floors. It feeds on food scraps and stored food, and may spread diseases. Some house mice have adapted to life in refrigerated food stores.

▲ **Field vole** 120–150mm
Occasionally seen in daylight. It feeds on plants and seeds, and can be a nuisance because it eats vegetables and flower bulbs. The vole's small ears, rounded nose and short tail distinguish it from mice.

▼ **Brown rat** 360–500mm
This pest has adapted very well to life in towns. It lives in drains and sewers, factories and wasteland, eats anything and scavenges in dustbins and waste tips. It damages stored food and carries diseases.

▲ **Black rat** 350–480mm
This unwelcome pest has been spread all over the world by ships. It lives in buildings, such as dockland warehouses. It can cause serious damage to stored food and spreads disease.

▲Grey squirrel 460–500mm
Originally from North America.
It is a popular animal in parks,
taking food from visitors. Like
the red squirrel, it is mainly
vegetarian and hoards food. It
sleeps in winter, but is active on
mild days.

▼ Long-eared bat 80–100mm
Can be distinguished by its broad
wings and long ears. This bat is
normally nocturnal and spends
the day hidden in a hollow tree,
or in a loft or church steeple. It
feeds on flying insects.

▲Red squirrel 370–500mm
This rodent eats seeds, fruit, tree-
buds and birds' eggs. In winter it
sleeps in a hole in a tree, and
wakes on sunny days.

▼ Pipistrelle bat 60–80mm
A furry bat, more often seen than
the long-eared bat because it flies
at dusk. It roosts in groups in
buildings during the day. In
winter it hibernates.

▲Rabbit 400mm
This furry pet can be a pest in the
countryside. In towns it lives on
commons, in parks, in suburban
areas with large gardens or on
railway embankments. It feeds
on a variety of plants, which can
make it unpopular with
gardeners.

▲Hedgehog 160–260mm
Hunts insects, worms and slugs
in the evening or early morning,
finding its food by smell. Its
spines protect it from enemies. It
hibernates in dry sheltered
places, such as in piles of leaves
or under sheds.

▼ Fox 100cm
This large animal eats small
mammals, particularly field
voles, but also scavenges from
dustbins and waste tips. The fox
often makes its home, called an
earth, by enlarging a rabbit hole.

▼ Badger 750–930mm
This large mammal is rarely
seen. It sometimes makes its
home, or sett, on a quiet railway
embankment. It is nocturnal, and
eats almost anything.

The road-side

Up to a quarter of the ground space in towns is taken up by roads and car parks. Even though most of the soil in these is covered by tarmac or concrete, many different plants and animals survive in these harsh conditions.

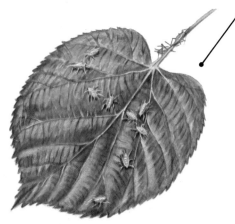

▲ Aphids on a lime leaf
Millions of aphids may live on a single large lime tree, feeding on its sap. As they feed, they produce a sugary liquid called honeydew. Ants feed on this, as do several fungi. The aphids are also eaten by insects and birds.

Roof tiles and walls are like the bare rock of mountains and sea cliffs. Very few plants live there. However, one group of plants that can grow in these dry conditions are the **lichens** (11) such as blackshields and yellowscales. Lichens are killed by pollution.

Walls also provide a niche for **plants** which need little soil. You may find fleshy-leaved stonecrop (10), with white or yellow flowers, and dainty ivy-leaved toadflax (14).

Spores

Germinating spore

Prothallus

Young fern plant

Adult fern fronds

16

▼ Privet hawkmoth caterpillar

One common hedge plant is privet, which provides food for these large green caterpillars. At the end of the summer, the caterpillar burrows into the soil and turns into a pupa. In spring the moth will emerge.

Small tough **plants** grow in cracks in the pavement and gutter. Plantains (20), dandelions (17), clover (18), daisies (19), shepherd's purse (15) and some grasses (26) all manage to flower in these tiny pockets of soil.

◀ Ferns

Some tough plants, such as bracken (13), can grow in gutters. Bracken is a fern. Tiny spores are blown into the gutter, where each grows into a small green heart-shaped plant called a prothallus. After a few weeks, a small fern plant begins to grow on the prothallus, which then disappears.

▶ Mosses

Mosses (8) grow in crevices in walls. Two of the commonest ones are wall screw moss (above) and silvery thread moss (below). The moss traps brick particles, which start to form soil.

Key

1 Lime
2 Swift
3 Pigeon
4 Cherry
5 Wallflower
6 Privet
7 Lime
8 Moss
9 Wolf spider
10 Stonecrop
11 Lichens
12 Starling
13 Bracken
14 Ivy-leaved toadflax
15 Shepherd's purse
16 Sparrow
17 Dandelion
18 Clover
19 Daisy
20 Plantain
21 Ivy
22 Zebra spider
23 Woodlice
24 Liverwort
25 Pied wagtail
26 Grass

Insects and other tiny animals

Invertebrates live everywhere. Some are large, others too small to see without a microscope. Some fly, others live on or under the ground.

*Not to scale. Adult body-length given.

▲ **Hawthorn shieldbug** 17mm
This common shieldbug has piercing and sucking mouthparts, and looks like a shield. It feeds on hawthorn berries. In spring it also eats leaves.

▲**Ichneumon fly** 17mm
Most ichneumon flies are parasites on other insects. The females lay their eggs in the body of a moth or butterfly larva. When the eggs hatch they feed on the body of the caterpillar. This ichneumon fly often flies into houses at dusk.

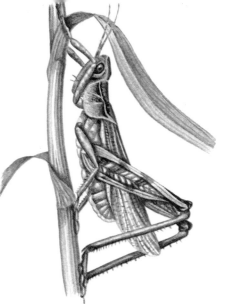

▲**Common field grasshopper** 17mm
Often seen or heard in summer in rough grass on wasteland. It eats plants, mainly grass, and is usually brown, sometimes with green patches.

▼ **Lime hawkmoth** 35mm
Adult moths fly at night in early summer. They vary in colour and pattern. The larvae are bright green with yellow markings, and feed on lime leaves.

▼ **Drone-fly** 25mm
This is a hover-fly, and can be seen flying or hovering in the garden on a warm summer day. It looks like a bee, but has no sting, and only one pair of wings.

▼ **Oak-apple gall wasp** 3mm
The female wasp lays eggs in the buds of the oak, which makes galls form. The larvae mature inside the galls and adult wasps emerge in summer.

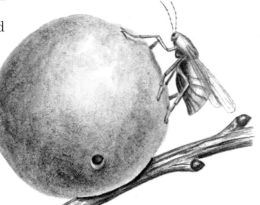

▼ **Wall brown butterfly** wingspan 47mm
On sunny days this butterfly can be seen flying on open grassy wasteland. Its larvae feed on grasses at night.

▲Common wasp 11–20mm
Wasps live in nests underground, or in walls. They live mainly on nectar and rotting fruit. They only sting in self-defence. The larvae are fed on flies.

▲Centipede 5–10mm
This is not an insect, because it has more than six legs. It spends the day hiding. At night it hunts spiders, insects and small slugs. It has one pair of legs on each body segment.

▼ Orb-web spider 5–12mm
This beautiful garden spider spins a large sticky web, and hides in nearby leaves. Insects are trapped in the web and the spider feeds on them.

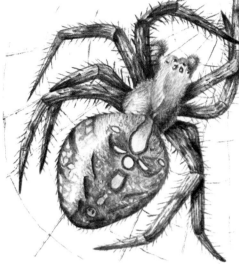

▲Red-tailed bumble bee 22mm
This large bee usually nests in an old mouse-hole underground, in colonies of several hundred bees. The larvae are fed on honey.

▲ Millipede 17–20m
This invertebrate is slower-moving than a centipede and usually eats rotting plants. It has two pairs of legs on each segment.

▼ Harvestman 4-9mm
The harvestman can be seen quite often in daylight. It runs over the ground or scrambles through plants hunting for the flies and ants which it eats.

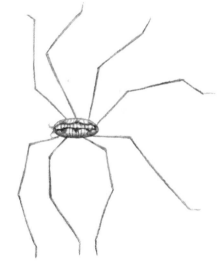

▼ Cockchafer, Maybug (male) 24mm
This large beetle flies at night and often crashes into lighted windows. The larvae live in the soil, feeding on grass roots. The male has 'fans' on his antennae.

▲Earwig 12mm
Feeds mainly on insects, which it hunts at night. Its name probably comes from its ear-shaped wings. The female earwig guards her eggs and young until they are fully grown.

Camouflage

Some animals avoid being eaten by being hard to see against their background.

The peppered moth often rests on silver birch trees during the day, and is white with black spots (**left**). In cities a new form has developed, which is black (**right**). This is so that the moth cannot be seen against the dirty tree-trunks.

Along the canal

Before the railways were built, canals were the most important means of transporting heavy goods. Today, most goods are carried by road or rail. However, many canals are still used, either for transport or by pleasure boats.

Others have become stretches of stagnant water. Where they run through industrial cities canals may be polluted. The cleaner a canal is, the more life it contains.

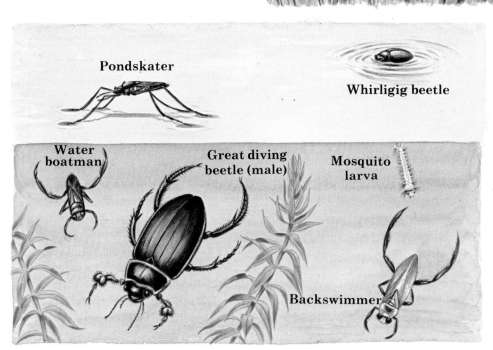

Pondskater

Whirligig beetle

Water boatman

Great diving beetle (male)

Mosquito larva

Backswimmer

▲ On the surface

Some animals live only on the surface of the water. Others swim freely, while some crawl on plants or the canal bottom.

One very common surface-animal is the pondskater (18). This insect skims about on the surface film, and can move very quickly to capture insects or other small animals at the surface of the water. The pondskater is often joined by groups of whirligig beetles (19) which swim in circles on the surface of the water.

◀ Underwater

Below the surface the canal teems with life. Many insects which swim freely have to return to the surface to obtain fresh supplies of air. The fiercest of these is the great diving beetle (24), which will attack fish much larger than itself.

Another active hunter is the backswimmer (22). Swimming upside-down, propelled by two long oar-like legs, the backswimmer hunts for tadpoles, beetle larvae and small fish. The water boatman (20) is smaller and flatter.

The canal and banks provide food and shelter for many **birds,** such as reed buntings (5) and moorhens (14).

Insects swarm above the water and are caught by swallows (3). Yellow wagtails (8) arrive in summer and feed on insects. Herons (7) fish in the shallows.

▼ Flatworms, snails, leeches
Flatworms (1) feed on water fleas and other small animals.

Snails eat small plants which grow on larger plants.

Leeches (2) attack fish, tadpoles and even snails, and suck out blood and body fluids.

Ramshorn snail

Wandering snail

Key

1 Alder	13 Arrowhead
2 Willow	14 Moorhen
3 Swallow	15 Starwort
4 Guelder rose	16 Yellow water-lily
5 Reed bunting	17 Ramshorn snail
6 Common reed	18 Pond skater
7 Heron	19 Whirligig beetle
8 Yellow wagtail	20 Water boatman
9 Rosebay willowherb	21 Mosquito larva
	22 Backswimmer
10 Comfrey	23 Carp
11 Rush	24 Great diving beetle
12 Great marsh sedge	25 Eel
	26 Canadian pondweed
	27 Yellow flag

◄ On the bottom
The water scorpion (1) hides in plants just below the surface, with a long breathing tube pushed up through the surface film. It seizes small animals such as fish and tadpoles. Dragonfly nymphs (2) also hunt among the plants and on the canal bed. They have extending lower jaws, called a mask, which they shoot out to seize passing animals.

Another crawling animal is the water louse (3). This relative of the woodlouse feeds on decaying animals and plants.

The banks are often covered with a thick mass of **plants** such as thistles, nettles, rosebay and great willowherb and meadowsweet. Trees that prefer damp soil, including willows (2) and alder (1), grow well on canal banks, as do many of the smaller hedgerow trees, such as wayfaring tree and guelder rose.

Water voles live among the plants, nesting in holes in the bank. These mammals swim very well. Their coats look silvery under water, as the fur traps bubbles of air.

Life in the water

Hundreds of different animals and plants live in a canal.

*Not to scale.

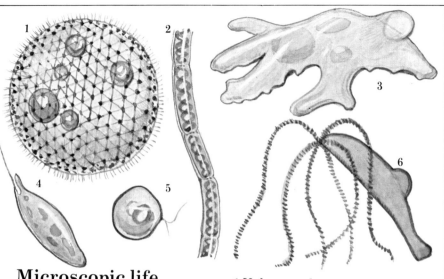

Microscopic life
Water is full of plants and animals which can only be seen properly under a microscope. They are the basic food for water-life.

1 Volvox, a plant-animal (x150). **2** Spirogyra, a plant (x500). **3** Amoeba (x200), **4** Euglena (x500), **5** Chlamydomonas (x700), **6** Hydra (x10), all animals.

▲**Water milfoil** life-size
A common water plant, which grows rooted in mud at the bottom of ponds, canals and streams. Its feathery leaves make a great deal of oxygen during daylight.

▲**Water starwort** life-size
Another common underwater plant which grows on mud. At the end of each stem are four leaves which grow in a star-shape.

▲**Canadian pondweed** life-size
You will find this plant in most freshwater habitats. It grows completely underwater except for its tiny pinkish flowers, which float on the surface.

▶**Great diving beetle** 25mm
One of the most savage underwater predators is the great diving beetle. Both the nymphs and adults are carnivorous and will attack larger animals.

▲**Flatworms: dugesia (top), polycelis (bottom)** 15mm
These are normally found under stones or on the underside of leaves. They feed on small animals and their eggs.

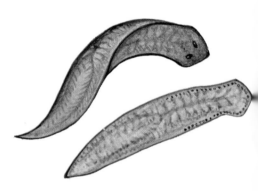

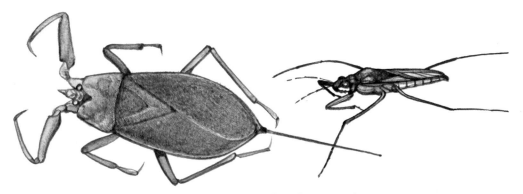

▲ **Damselfly laying eggs**
45mm
Damselfly eggs hatch into wingless nymphs, which live underwater until ready to become adults.

▲**Water scorpion (left)** 25mm, **pondskater (right)** 20mm
The water scorpion and pondskater are both bugs. Their front wings are toughened and protect the thinner hind wings.

The slow-moving water scorpion lives below the surface, and breathes through its long tube. The quicker pondskater skims over the surface film on its long legs. Both eat other insects.

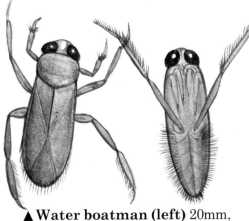

▲ **Water boatman (left)** 20mm, **backswimmer (right)** 20mm
The water boatman looks silver underwater, and the backswimmer swims on its back. Both are fierce hunters. They pierce small animals with their sharp mouthparts and suck out their juices.

▲**Newts** life-size
The palmate newt (top) is the smallest of these three newts. The male has webbed hind feet. The common newt (bottom) is slightly larger. In the breeding season the male grows a crest from nose to tail. The largest of all is the great crested newt (right), which has a high, ragged crest.

Newts live on land but return to the water to breed. The great crested newt spends more time in the water than do the other two.

▲**Water spider** 8-15mm
This is the only spider in the world which can live underwater. The water spider spins a web on water plants and fills it with air from the surface.

▼ **Common frog (left)** 10cm, **common toad (right)** 12cm
The common frog has a smooth moist skin and normally lives in very damp places near water.

The toad has a rough, warty skin and is often found in dry places. The frog usually hops and the toad usually walks. Both feed on insects and breed in water.

23

Birds

Town birds come from many different habitats but all have learned to live with people.

*Not to scale. Adult body-length given.

▲House sparrow 14–15cm
This is a true town bird. It spends most of its life near to houses, and lives almost entirely on scraps from houses. It makes an untidy nest in a hole, often in a building.

▲House martin 12–13cm
Originally a cliff and cave-nesting species. House martins live in mud nests which they build under the eaves of houses. They migrate south in autumn.

▲Feral pigeon 31–34cm
These large birds are descended from rock doves. They vary in colour and pattern, and can be seen everywhere in towns. They nest on buildings.

▲Blue tit 11–12cm
This woodland bird is often seen in town gardens. It is mainly an insect eater, but also takes peanuts and bacon rind from bird tables in winter.

▲Blackbird 24–26cm
The cock bird is black with a yellow bill, and the hen is brown. It feeds on insects, earthworms, fruit and seeds, and has a beautiful song.

▲Tree sparrow 13–14cm
Sometimes seen in parks and gardens. It is smaller than the house sparrow, has a black spot on each cheek, a smaller black bib, and the crown of its head is chestnut.

▲ Great tit 14cm
This common garden bird is larger than the blue tit. It is often seen looking for seeds or insects in low bushes or on the ground.

▲Jackdaw 33cm
This bird lives in colonies near old buildings, such as churches, or in parks with old trees. It eats mainly insects, seeds, eggs and young birds.

▲Starling 21–22cm
Thousands of these noisy birds roost on large buildings in town centres, and in the trees of town squares. Many may fly to the country to feed each day and return at night.

◄Pied wagtail 18cm
This perky bird can be seen chasing winged insects in parks and even on quite busy roads. It nests in a bank or wall. The female's back is grey.

▼ Greenfinch 14.5cm
This finch is now commoner in towns than it is in the country. It often nests in garden shrubs, and feeds mainly on seeds and tree-buds.

▼ Bullfinch 15cm
A bird of the suburbs, with a short, sharp, strong bill. In spring it often eats buds from fruit trees, destroying the crop before it has formed.

▲ Robin 14cm
This woodland bird is often seen in gardens, picking up worms and insects from newly-dug soil. It also eats seeds and fruit. The male is very aggressive.

▲ Chaffinch 15cm
This common finch can be seen in suburban gardens and parks. It is a seed-eater and will visit the bird table in winter. The young are fed on insects.

▲ Goldfinch 12cm
This acrobatic and attractive little bird can sometimes be seen in groups on derelict land and rubbish tips. It eats mainly thistle seeds.

▲ Tawny owl 38cm
A large bird with a quavering 'hoo-hoo' call. It rests in old trees during the day. At night it hunts mice, voles and other small animals.

▲ Carrion crow 47cm
The carrion crow is larger than the jackdaw, and is completely black. The rook is similar but has bare patches round its beak.

Beaks

There is a close link between the shape of a bird's beak and the type of food that it eats.

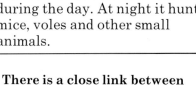

1 The mallard's flat beak is used to skim food, such as plants, from the water.

2 With its hooked beak the kestrel tears the flesh of the animals it eats.

3 The swallow's fine beak can open wide to seize insects as it flies.

5 The pigeon's beak enables it to pick up quite large seeds and scraps.

4 The strong beak of the greenfinch can crack quite large seeds.

6 The wren has a long fine beak, with which it probes for insects in tree bark.

25

Inside a house

People share their houses with many other animals and plants. Some are welcome. Pets and house plants are brought into the home deliberately. Some animals, like the silverfish and firebrat, move in almost unnoticed. Others, including fleas, bugs and lice, are pests.

All thrive on the extra warmth and shelter provided by the house and its inhabitants.

▼ Uninvited plants

Most unwanted plants are harmless, though in time they may damage brickwork. **Lichens** like the ones below often grow on the roofs of old houses. There are many different species, varying in shape and colour. Each is two plants, a fungus living with an alga.

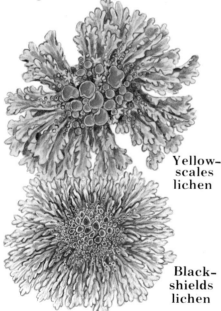

Yellow-scales lichen

Black-shields lichen

Liverworts may grow on damp walls, such as behind leaking drainpipes. They are usually flat green plants with curled leaves.

One plant is very unwelcome. **Dry rot fungus** (4) lives on old wood. If it gets into floorboards or roof supports it can seriously damage them.

Key

1 Mealy bug
2 Whitefly
3 Silverfish
4 Dry rot fungus
5 Brown rat
6 House spider
7 House mouse and nest
8 Ant
9 Flour beetle, cockroach, etc.
10 Cat flea

▲ Kitchen visitors

The kitchen is the most popular part of the house for many animals. Food is usually plentiful, and it is warm. Grain weevils and flour beetles (9) attack dry food. Cockroaches (9) feed on almost any food scraps. Ants (8) carry food away to their nests. Silverfish (3) and firebrats scavenge for crumbs of food.

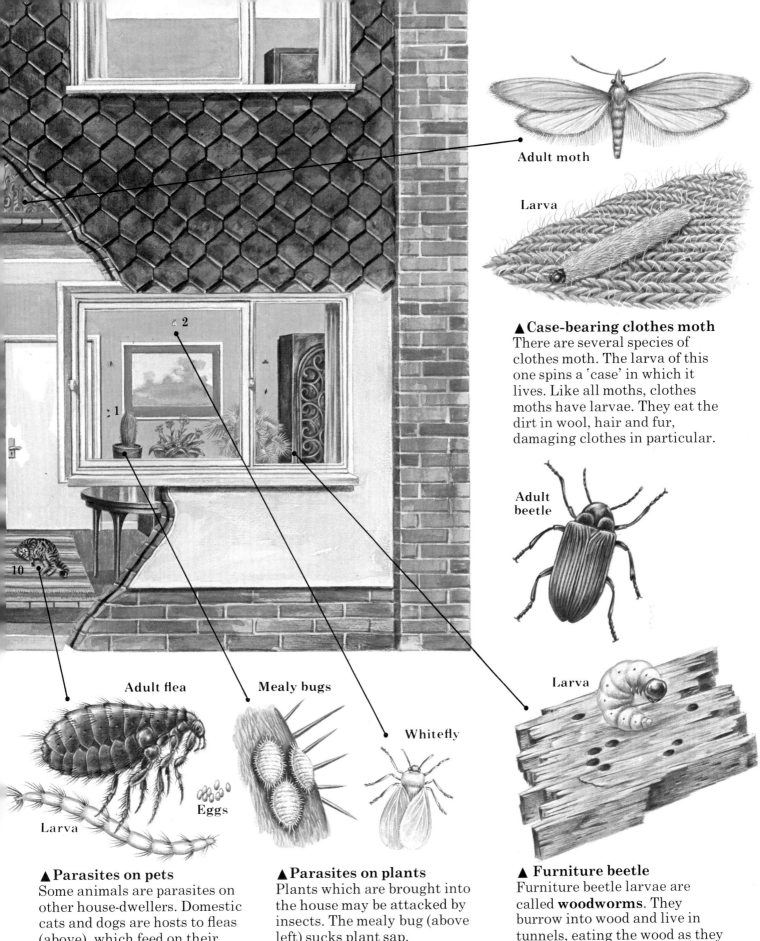

Adult moth

Larva

▲Case-bearing clothes moth
There are several species of
clothes moth. The larva of this
one spins a 'case' in which it
lives. Like all moths, clothes
moths have larvae. They eat the
dirt in wool, hair and fur,
damaging clothes in particular.

Adult
beetle

Adult flea

Mealy bugs

Whitefly

Eggs

Larva

Larva

▲Parasites on pets
Some animals are parasites on
other house-dwellers. Domestic
cats and dogs are hosts to fleas
(above), which feed on their
blood. They have hard, flat
bodies which slide easily through
fur, and they can jump enormous
distances.

▲Parasites on plants
Plants which are brought into
the house may be attacked by
insects. The mealy bug (above
left) sucks plant sap.
  Whiteflies (above right) are
tiny two-winged insects, which
look like minute moths. They
weaken plants.

▲ Furniture beetle
Furniture beetle larvae are
called **woodworms**. They
burrow into wood and live in
tunnels, eating the wood as they
go. Small round holes in
furniture and small piles of
sawdust on the floor show that
woodworms are at work.

Who lives in your house?

No matter how clean it is, any house has uninvited inhabitants.

*Not to scale. Adult body-length given.

▲**Cellar spider** 8–10mm
This spider spins a web near the ceiling and can often be seen hanging upside down in the corner of a room. The female holds the egg cocoon in her jaws until the tiny spiders hatch.

▲**Bluebottle** 8–11mm
A large, hairy, blue-bodied fly, whose wings make a buzzing sound. The one found in houses is usually the female, which comes indoors searching for meat on which to lay its eggs. It carries disease.

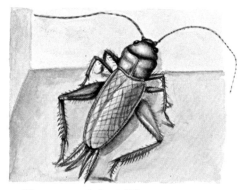

▲**House cricket** 20mm
This cricket lives in old houses, where it is active at night, scavenging for food scraps. It is less common than it was, but can still be found outdoors in the warmth of rubbish tips.

▲**House spider** 11–14mm
This large brown spider is the one which often falls into the bath. It spins a large, matted sheet web which is rolled up to form a tunnel in one corner. It feeds on flies trapped in its web.

▲**Housefly** 6–9mm
This greyish fly is very common in houses. The adults lay their eggs on decaying matter or excrement, where the larvae hatch and develop. Flies carry diseases.

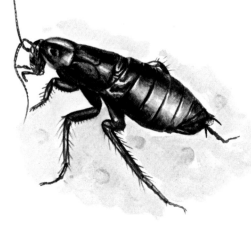

▲**Common cockroach** 20–30mm
This insect feeds on food scraps at night. It thrives in dirty buildings, particularly dirty restaurants, and on waste tips, from which it carries diseases.

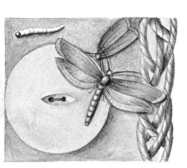

▲**Clothes moth** 11–15mm
This common moth can be found in summer. Its larvae feed mainly on dirty woollen clothes, making holes in them. They also attack fur and feathers, but not synthetic materials.

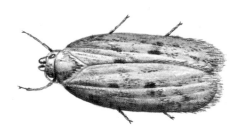

▲**Brown house moth** 20–23mm
This nocturnal moth enters houses in summer to lay its eggs. The larvae feed on scraps of animal or vegetable matter between floorboards and often damage carpets as well.

▲Silverfish 10mm
This small, wingless insect is common in houses, particularly in kitchens and bathrooms. It is active at night and will run for shelter when lights are switched on. It feeds on tiny scraps of food or wallpaper paste.

▲Firebrat 12mm
Like the silverfish, this is a bristletail, a type of wingless insect. It feeds on tiny food scraps, and needs warm surroundings in order to survive. This means that it is often only found near fireplaces or stoves.

▲Headlouse 1–3mm
This small louse is a parasite. It lives on humans, among hairs on the head. It pierces the skin and sucks blood. The white eggs (nits) are usually attached to hair or clothes. Headlice spread diseases.

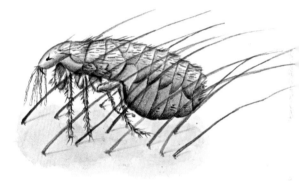

▲Black ant 4–9mm
Although it nests in gardens, the black ant often enters houses searching for food. It carries sugar and other loose foods back to its nest.

▲Bedbug 5–6mm
This bug is less common than it was. By day it hides in cracks between floor-boards or behind skirting boards. At night it sucks blood from sleeping people.

▲Flea 2-4mm
This irritating parasite sucks human blood, leaving an itchy bump. It can only live in dirty conditions, and is less common than it was.

▲Woodworm 4–5mm
This is a furniture beetle. The larva bores into wood, leaving small round holes and piles of dust. It can be introduced into a house in old second-hand furniture. The adults fly at night.

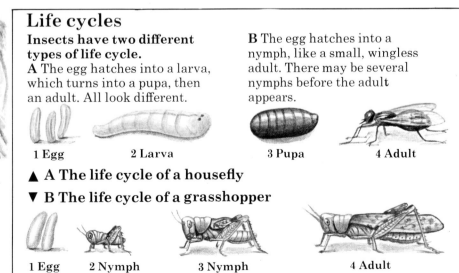

Life cycles
Insects have two different types of life cycle.
A The egg hatches into a larva, which turns into a pupa, then an adult. All look different.

B The egg hatches into a nymph, like a small, wingless adult. There may be several nymphs before the adult appears.

1 Egg   2 Larva   3 Pupa   4 Adult

▲ **A The life cycle of a housefly**

▼ **B The life cycle of a grasshopper**

1 Egg   2 Nymph   3 Nymph   4 Adult

Looking at ponds

A pond is a shallow hole in the ground which has filled with water. Water plants and insects appear. Frogs come to breed, birds come to nest and drink. Gradually the pond fills with life.

Most ponds were made by people. Some are ornamental, others were dug as drinking-places for cattle or coach-horses. Larger ponds form where chalk and gravel has been dug out.

Every pond is different. One which is overshadowed will have very little life. Rotting leaves make a scum on the surface, keeping oxygen out. Mosquito larvae use tubes to breathe through this, and a few animals feed on the smelly black mud.

A pond in the open gets plenty of sunlight, so that green plants can grow. The water is full of oxygen, so that animals can breathe. Many different plants and animals live there.

▼ **How a pond turns into land.**

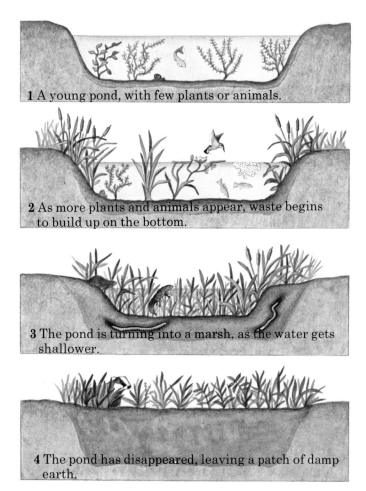

1 A young pond, with few plants or animals.

2 As more plants and animals appear, waste begins to build up on the bottom.

3 The pond is turning into a marsh, as the water gets shallower.

4 The pond has disappeared, leaving a patch of damp earth.

▼ **A food pyramid (not to scale). Each arrow means 'eaten by'.**

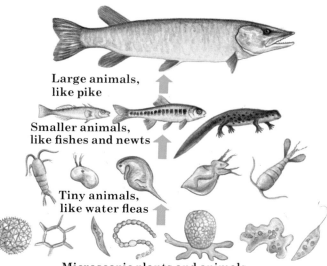

Large animals, like pike

Smaller animals, like fishes and newts

Tiny animals, like water fleas

Microscopic plants and animals

All the plants and animals in a pond eat or are eaten by each other. This can be shown in a diagram, like the **food pyramid** above. The tiniest plants, at the bottom, make food using the energy in sunlight. They are eaten by tiny animals. Larger animals, like small fishes and newts, eat them. They are then eaten by large animals, like the pike at the top.

Another way of showing how energy is passed on is in a **food chain** (below). When the pike dies its body rots, and is used by minute plants and animals to make food.

▼ **A food chain (not to scale).**

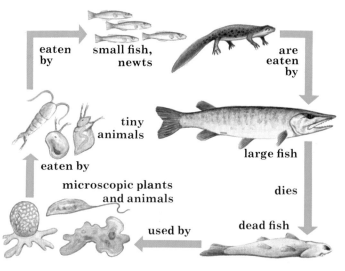

eaten by — small fish, newts — are eaten by

tiny animals

large fish

eaten by

microscopic plants and animals

dies

used by — dead fish

◀ **From pond to dry land**
Ponds slowly fill in and become dry land. A young pond (**1**) is clear and open. Plants grow in the shallow water at the edge (**2**). As they die their remains form a layer on the bottom. This gets thicker and the water becomes shallower (**3**). Plants grow in the middle of the pond. The pond fills in completely (**4**).

From mountains to the sea

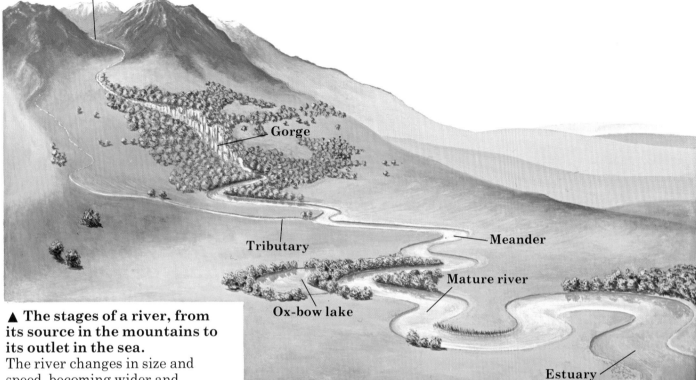

Mountain stream

Gorge

Tributary

Meander

Mature river

Ox-bow lake

Estuary

Sea

▲ **The stages of a river, from its source in the mountains to its outlet in the sea.**
The river changes in size and speed, becoming wider and slower the further it goes.

It is also affected by the country it flows through, and by the weather. After a storm it is deeper and faster, but it may almost dry up in a long hot summer.

As the river changes, so do the plants and animals living in or by it. Some prefer deep, slow-flowing muddy water. Others live in shallow, fast-flowing clear water.

How rivers form

Most rivers start high up in mountains and hills, where the rainfall is heavy, and where there may be melting snow. Some of the water soaks into the ground and some gathers in hollows and between stones, making pools. Some runs over the ground in small channels. These channels join up and a **stream** is formed.

The stream rushes downward, carrying pebbles and gravel. They carve a channel into the soil and soft rock. As the stream moves downhill it is joined by others. Soon the young **river** is a torrent cascading down the hillside.

The river leaves narrow V-shaped valleys as it wears the ground away beneath it. Stones and boulders are swept along, and pile up, making rapids. Soft rock is worn away, leaving deep **gorges** in the hillside.

The ground starts to level out as the river leaves the hills. Large sidestreams, called

tributaries, join the main stream. The river widens, becomes deeper, and flows more slowly and smoothly.

The valley sides are now gentle slopes. The **mature river** flows too slowly to carry boulders, but mud and sand are still swept along.

As the land becomes flatter the river starts to curve from side to side. It forms large loops, called **meanders**. On the outside curve of each meander the river flows fast, eating away the bank and making the loop larger. On the inside curve it flows slowly. Sediment (mud and sand) which has been eroded (cut away) from the banks is dropped here. Eventually the meander will be cut off from the river and form an **ox-bow lake**.

The river has become wide and slow-flowing by the time it reaches the sea. It is carrying huge amounts of soil, which has been eroded from the banks. Much of this is dropped in the **estuary**, where it forms mudflats and sandbanks.

A mountain stream

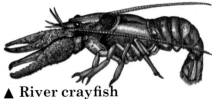

▲ **River crayfish**
The crayfish is a large crustacean, up to 6cm long.

During the day the crayfish hides under stones or in a burrow in the bank. At night it crawls over the bottom, feeding on snails, and insect larvae. It only lives in clean water.

▲ An adult **salmon** (9) rising to take a mayfly. It has returned from the sea to the stream where it was hatched.

No one knows how salmon find their way back to their native streams. They may remember the smell of the water, or use the sun's position.

▲ On the stony bed of the stream a **stone loach** (19) is looking for food. It eats stonefly and mayfly nymphs, and usually hunts at night.

Perched on a nearby rock is a male **ring ouzel** (11), looking for insects. It has a clear fluting call, and is a summer visitor. In winter it flies as far south as Africa.

On the other side of the stream is a patch of boggy ground, where **cotton grass** (3) grows. In late spring its seedheads burst, so that it looks like cotton wool, and the fluffy white seeds are blown away.

Key		
	9 Salmon	18 Caddis-fly larva
1 Rushes	10 Mayfly	19 Stone loach
2 Hawthorn	11 Ring ouzel	20 Liverworts
3 Cotton grass	12 Freshwater shrimp	21 Water moss
4 White willow	13 Miller's thumb	22 Brown trout
5 Heather	14 Crayfish	23 Grey wagtail
6 Bracken	15 Minnow	24 Eel
7 Royal fern	16 Mayfly nymph	25 Horse leech
8 Hart's-tongue fern	17 Stonefly nymph	26 Dipper

High in the mountains streams rush down rocky slopes, into rock pools and over shallow rapids. The current is too fast for many plants to take root on the stony bed, and few tiny animals can live here.

The water is cold, but clear and full of dissolved oxygen. The animals and plants here prefer these conditions.

▼ **Bracken** (6) and **heather** (5) cover the mountainside. Bracken can grow up to 2.5 metres high, and gives shelter to many small animals, such as rabbits.

Heather is a tough, low plant. In late summer it has purple flowers, loved by bees.

In the damp soil near the water grow **hart's-tongue fern** (8) and **royal fern** (7). Ferns have no flowers. They spread by spores, which grow on the underside of the leaves in autumn. When ripe the spores blow away.

▼ **Buffalo gnat and pupa**
Swarms of these tiny black biting flies gather near water in the summer. Their larvae live in running water, attached to stones.

Each larva turns into a pupa, and spins a silken cocoon fastened to a stone, and filled with air. When the adult fly is ready to emerge it floats to the surface in a bubble of air and flies away.

▲ The long green fronds of **water moss** (21) trail in the fast-flowing water. Its Latin name is *Fontinalis antipyretica*. The second word means 'against fire', because it burns very badly.

The **brown trout** (22) likes fast-flowing, cold water, which contains a lot of oxygen. It is well camouflaged by its spots.

▲ A **dipper** (26) walks underwater. It can swim and dive well, and finds its food among the stones on the stream-bed.

Above it a **grey wagtail** (23) is perched on a rock. This is a male (cock) bird, which has a black summer bib. The wagtail eats insects, which it snatches as they fly above the water.

▼ **Horse leech**
A horse leech eating a river snail. It also eats worms and larvae, which it swallows whole.

Leeches are very common in fresh water. They vary from 1cm to 15cm long.

Water-birds

Freshwater habitats are full of birds. They come to drink, to bathe, and to feed on the great variety of plants and animals there.

Some, like mallard, live on the water. They have developed webbed feet to help them swim. Others, like herons, live on land but visit water to feed.

*Not to scale. The size given is the body-length of a mature adult.

Male   Female

▲ **Pied wagtail** 18cm
A perky bird, often seen by rivers wagging its long tail, or running along the bank. It eats small insects such as flies, beetles and moths, which it catches on the wing.

▲ **Grey wagtail** 18cm
One of the most colourful wagtails, seen near fast-flowing water. It eats mostly insects, such as flies, nymphs and small beetles. The male (left) has a black bib in summer.

▲ **Kingfisher** 16.5cm
Usually seen as a flash of blue darting along a stream or river. It dives from a perch and spears small fishes, which it swallows head first so that the scales lie flat.

▲ **Reed warbler** 12.5cm
Lives in reed-beds, where it eats flies and moths, and berries in autumn. Its cup-shaped nest is woven round reed stems. In winter it flies south, sometimes as far as Africa.

▲ **Heron** 90cm
A tall, silent, wading bird seen by rivers, lake and ponds. It stands on one leg or stalks small animals, such as frogs, fishes and water-voles. It has a slow, flapping flight and nests in colonies in trees.

Waterbirds in flight

You can identify birds by the way they fly, and the shape of their bodies.

1 Mallard   2 Coot   3 Goose
4 Mute swan   5 Heron   6 Crane

1 Pointed wings, flaps fast.
2 Round wings, legs trail, weak flier. 3 Long neck, often in flocks. 4 Long neck, slow flight.

5 Head drawn back, legs trail, slow flight. 6 Neck out-stretched, legs trail, slow flight.

▲ **Dipper** 18cm
A chunky little bird, seen
perched on rocks or flying low
and fast along mountain streams.
Its brown and white plumage
hide it well among the brown
rocks and white water.

    It catches insects, tadpoles and
small fishes underwater.

▲ **Snipe** 37cm
A striped bird, often seen in
marshy ground, using its long
bill to probe for worms, snails
and insect larvae. When
disturbed it flies up with a harsh
call. In the breeding season the
tail feathers of the male make a
bleating sound in flight.

▲ **Water rail** 28cm
Seen at dusk and dawn, hunting
in reed-beds for tiny animals
such as spiders, freshwater
shrimps and worms. It darts from
cover to cover with a high-
stepping walk or flies for a few
seconds. You may hear its high
sharp cry in the evening.

Male

Chicks

▲ **Mallard** 58cm
A common duck, seen swimming
on ponds, lakes and rivers or
flying overhead. It 'up-ends' or
dabbles in the water to find food,
mainly plants. The male (bottom)
is called a drake, and is brightly
coloured.

▲ **Coot** 38cm
A large bird, often seen
swimming on lakes or slow-
flowing rivers, or grazing on the
banks. It eats plants and small
water animals, such as tadpoles.
When disturbed it gives a loud,
high-pitched cry.

▲ **Moorhen** 35cm
A large bird, seen swimming or
diving near the banks of lakes,
ponds and slow-flowing rivers. It
eats seeds, water plants, worms,
snails and insect larvae. When
alarmed it can sink, leaving only
its bill above water.

A river

As the river flows downwards the ground becomes flatter. Trees and bushes grow on the banks, some planted there to stop the soil crumbling away.

The water flows more slowly, is warmer and cloudy. Water plants can take root on the muddy bottom. They give shelter to small animals, such as diving beetles, and to fish like roach and bream.

▲ **A sand martin feeding its young**
Sand martins are brown, with white underparts and short tails. They nest in large colonies in sandy river banks.

Both male and female dig a metre-long tunnel into the bank. Then they hollow out a chamber and line it to make the nest. The young birds are fed on insects which the parents catch as they fly over the water.

The sharp hooks with which the larva attaches itself to the fish

A larva living on a dorsal fin

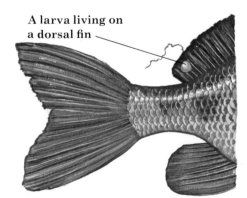

◀▲ **Swan mussel larva**
Swan mussels live on the muddy beds of ponds, lakes and rivers, and are up to 20cm long.

After laying her eggs, the female keeps them in her gills until spring. The larvae then swim out and hook on to a passing fish. They live on the fish for 2 to 3 weeks and then fall to the bottom, where they develop into mussels.

▲ A **pike** (16) swims fast after the **roach**. It has been hiding in the water plants, camouflaged by its patterned skin. Nothing can escape from its backward-sloping upper teeth.

Swimming above are two **great crested grebes** (11). They are in their summer plumage, with ruffs and ear-tufts. These are used in the courtship display which these birds perform.

▲ Emperor dragonfly laying eggs

After mating both the male and female fly to an egg-laying site, often a plant at the edge of the water. The female makes a slit in the stem and lays her eggs in it. When they hatch, the nymphs crawl into the water.

▼ A sponge colony

Sponges are tiny animals which cannot move. They live in colonies on stones, leaves or plant stems. They take food and oxygen from the water passing through them.

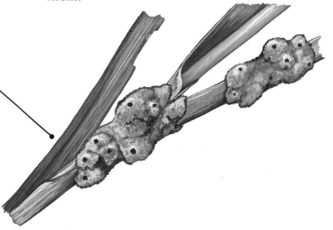

▲ The **otter** (25) is a superb swimmer and diver, with a short waterproof coat, streamlined body, webbed feet and a rudder-like tail. It can shut its ears and nostrils underwater. It usually hunts at night, and is very shy.

Skimming over the water is a **swallow** (12). Its tiny beak opens very wide to snatch insects, and its curved wings help it to change direction quickly.

Key

1 Crack willow	**9** Midges	**19** Perch
2 Swifts	**10** Teal	**20** Reedmace
3 White willow	**11** Great crested grebe	**21** Marestail
4 Alder	**12** Swallow	**22** Gudgeon
5 Mute swan	**13** Mayfly	**23** Shrew
6 Sand martin	**14** Emperor dragonfly	**24** Spiked water milfoil
7 Bulrush	**15** Water crowfoot	**25** Otter
8 Stonefly	**16** Pike	**26** Sponge
	17 Roach	**27** Canadian pondweed
	18 Dace	**28** Stone loach

Fishes

The fishes living in fresh waters can be as tiny as minnows or as large as pike. Some, like trout, prefer clear, cold, fast-running mountain streams. Others, like bream, prefer muddy, warm, slow-flowing lowland rivers or lakes.

*Not to scale. The size given is the body-length of a mature adult.

▲ **Barbel** 75-90cm
A large fish which lives in clear, fairly fast-flowing rivers with gravel bottoms. At night it hunts for food on the bottom, using its barbels to find worms, molluscs and insect larvae. During the day it rests in deep water near the bank.

▲ **Gudgeon** 10–15cm
A small fish, varying from grey-green to blackish-grey. Usually found in shallow water over gravel. It swims in small shoals close to the bottom and uses its feeler-like barbels to find food. It eats mostly insect larvae, shrimps and plants.

▲ **Chub** 35–50cm
Lives in clear rivers and streams, and varies in colour from dark green to greyish blue. The young live in shoals, but the adult fish is solitary, living in deep water near river banks. It eats mainly small fishes, crayfish, insects and plants.

Male in breeding colours

▲ **Minnow** 5–7cm
A tiny fish, often seen in large shoals of up to 100 fishes near the surface of shallow water. It eats insect larvae, tiny crustaceans and algae. In winter it lives in deeper water.

In summer the male changes to his breeding colours: green sides with black bars, scarlet belly and bronze-green head.

▲ **Grayling** 30–45cm
A slim fish, which you can recognize by its long dorsal fin. It lives in fast-flowing rivers and mountain lakes, often in small shoals. Most of the animals it eats live on the bottom, such as insect larvae, snails and freshwater shrimps.

▲ **Perch** 20–35cm
You can recognise this fish by the dark bars on its sides. The perch lives in deep water in rivers and lakes, often among weeds. It eats crustaceans, such as freshwater shrimps, the larvae of insects such as water beetles, and small fishes.

▲ **Pike** 40–100cm
A large fish, found in rivers and lakes. It is usually greenish, with gold spots and bars on its sides. This pattern helps to hide the pike as it waits among water plants for smaller fishes. It is a fierce hunter and sometimes eats water voles or ducklings.

▲ **Roach** 15–30cm
A medium-sized fish which lives in slow-flowing rivers and lakes. The young eat small crustaceans, such as freshwater shrimps. The adults eat mainly plants, with some insect larvae and snails. In colder weather roach often stop feeding.

▲ **Silver bream** 15cm
A rounded, humpbacked fish which lives in weedbeds near the bottom of rivers and deep lakes. It feeds on insect larvae and molluscs.

During the breeding season shoals gather in shallow water. The fish are very active and will leap out of the water and splash at the surface.

▲ **Brown trout** 18–35cm
Brown trout live in cold, fast-flowing water, usually in mountain rivers and lakes. They eat insects, insect larvae, crustaceans and smaller fishes. River trout have red spots and greenish-brown sides. Lake trout are usually smaller than river trout, and are often silver with black spots.

▲ **Dace** 20–25cm
Lives in fairly fast-flowing rivers and streams, and in some lakes. It prefers clean, shallow water and is often found in large shoals near the surface.

The dace eats snails, insects, freshwater shrimps and plants. It moves into shallow water over gravel or stones to spawn.

▲ **Miller's thumb** 10cm
A small fish, also called a bullhead, with a flattened head. Its colour varies from dark grey to brown.

It is usually found in fast-flowing water, hiding under stones during the day. At night it hunts slow-moving animals such as insect larvae, which it swallows whole.

▲ **Stone loach** 10cm
A small, rounded fish whose back varies in colour from dark olive to blue. It lives in rivers, streams and ponds.

The stone loach hides in a hollow under stones on the bottom during the day. At night it hunts insect larvae and crustaceans, which it finds on the bottom.

▲ **Common bream** 30–40cm
A dull bronze or grey fish which looks like the silver bream but is more common. It lives in large slow-moving rivers, lakes and reservoirs.

At night it feeds in the mud on the bottom. It eats small animals such as worms, insects, insect larvae and molluscs.

The parts of a fish

All fishes have the same parts, though they may look different. For instance, part of the dorsal fin of a stickleback is split into spines.

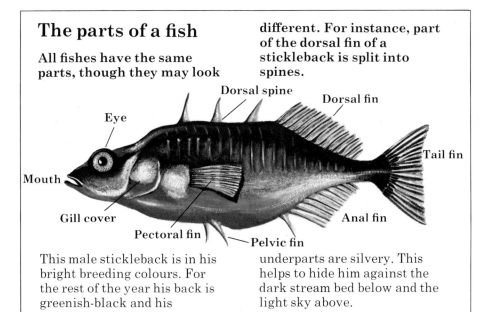

This male stickleback is in his bright breeding colours. For the rest of the year his back is greenish-black and his underparts are silvery. This helps to hide him against the dark stream bed below and the light sky above.

▲ **Eel** Male 30–50cm, female 90–150cm
Eels hatch as leaf-shaped larvae near the Sargasso Sea. Currents carry them to European coastal waters, where they change into elvers, about 10 cm long. These swim up into rivers and streams, where they become adults. They eat almost anything.

Water plants

Plants grow in water in several different ways. Some, like water-lilies, grow in deep water, rooted in the mud. The roots of floating plants, like duckweed, hang free.

Plants like arrowhead are rooted near the water's edge. Right at the edge grow tall plants.

*Not to scale. The height of upright plants is given.

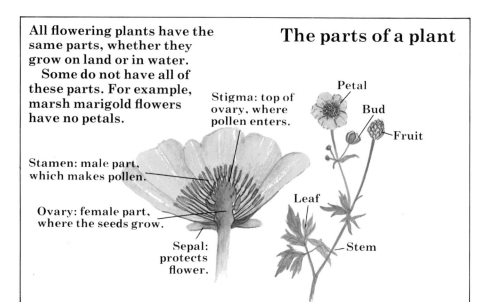

All flowering plants have the same parts, whether they grow on land or in water.

Some do not have all of these parts. For example, marsh marigold flowers have no petals.

The parts of a plant

Stigma: top of ovary, where pollen enters.

Petal

Bud

Fruit

Stamen: male part, which makes pollen.

Ovary: female part, where the seeds grow.

Leaf

Stem

Sepal: protects flower.

▲ **Water dropwort** 60cm
A member of the parsley family, with a smooth, hollow stem and fern-like leaves. It grows in ditches and shallow ponds. In summer it has large branched heads of tiny pinkish-white flowers.

▲ **Water plantain** 100cm
A tall, upright plant rooted in the mud at the edge of ponds, ditches and streams.

The broad leaves are held out of the water on long stalks. The three-petalled white flowers only open in the afternoon.

▲ **Arrowhead** 100cm
The name comes from the shape of the upper leaves. The lower ones are ribbon-like, and trail underwater. The male flowers are white with a purple centre, but the female flowers have no petals.

▲ **Watercress** 15-60cm
A wild herb, which grows in shallow water. Clusters of four-petalled white flowers are followed by long thin green seedpods. It is the same as the plant which we eat in salads, but should not be eaten.

▲ **Sweet flag** 100cm
A tall plant, found by ponds, canals and rivers. Sometimes it grows a tight spike of tiny flowers. Its leaves smell of tangerines when crushed. In medieval times they were used to scent rooms.

▲ **Bistort**
Another name for this plant is snakeweed. When it grows in water it has smooth floating leaves (shown here). On land it has hairy leaves. Both forms have clusters of reddish-white flowers.

▲ **Marestail** 75cm
The unbranched, erect stems can be seen in ponds and slow-moving water. The stiff thin leaves grow in whorls round the stem. In summer tiny green flowers appear where the leaves join the stem.

▲ **Water crowfoot**
Grows in ponds, streams and shallow rivers. The underwater leaves are fern-like, but the floating ones are glossy and like clover leaves. It is a member of the buttercup family, and has white buttercup-like flowers.

▲ **Spiked water milfoil**
The long, flexible stems grow underwater, rooted in the mud in ponds and shallow streams. The flowers appear above water, with the red male flowers higher than the female ones. It is pollinated by the wind.

▲ **Broad-leaved pondweed**
Found in most fresh waters. The floating leaves are large and oval but the submerged ones are long and thin. The tiny, greenish flowers have no petals. They grow clustered on tall spikes above the water.

▲ **Frogbit**
A floating plant, which has kidney-shaped leaves and white flowers above water. In autumn it grows shoots which then sink to the bottom. In spring they rise to the surface and grow into new plants.

▲ **White water-lily**
A beautiful plant, which grows rooted in the mud at the bottom of rivers, lakes and ponds. The leaves and flowers float on the surface during the day. At night the flowers close and sink below the water.

▲ **Canadian pondweed**
Grows in still water and spreads very fast. The purplish flowers float on the surface but the stem and leaves are underwater. In winter buds grow on the roots and stems. They drop off and grow into new plants.

▲ **Hornwort**
This is a free-floating plant which grows completely underwater. Pollen is carried from male flowers to female flowers by water. It has stiff, finely-divided leaves and is found in still water.

▲ **Duckweed**
The green covering on many ponds and ditches is made up of thousands of tiny plants. Each one is a single leaf-like disc with a root. It spreads by growing buds, which break off and form new plants.

Insects and other tiny animals

Animals without backbones are called invertebrates. They are all quite small, and many have a hard covering. Insects are one large group of invertebrates.

Many invertebrates live near water. Some, like slugs, have to keep moist. Others, like dragonflies, spend the first part of their lives in water.

Since they are small, invertebrates are often eaten by other animals.

*Not to scale. The size given is the body-length of a mature adult.

▲ **Common damselfly** 35mm, wingspan 45mm
Found flying near still and slow-flowing water during the summer. Its green or brown nymphs live underwater for about two years. Nymphs and adults both eat smaller insects.

▲ **Large red damselfly** 35mm, wingspan 45mm
Like all damselflies, the common red rests with its wings folded together above its back. It is seen flying over lakes and slow-flowing rivers. The nymphs are short and dark brown.

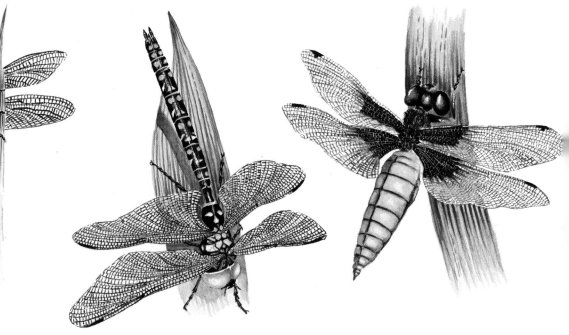

▲ **Golden-ringed dragonfly** 70mm, wingspan 95mm
A large, powerful flier which hunts insects over fast-flowing rivers and streams during the summer, and can be seen after dark. Its nymph is dark brown and hairy, and hides in mud.

▲ **Common aeshna** 70mm, wingspan 95mm
A long slim dragonfly, common near water in mountain and moorland areas. This is a male, with blue eyes and body. The females and young males are usually green or yellow.

▲ **Broad-bodied libellula** 45mm, wingspan 70mm
A darter dragonfly, which makes short flights from a perch. It has a broad, flat body. The male is blue, and the female is brown. It flies near still or slow-moving water.

The life cycle of a dragonfly

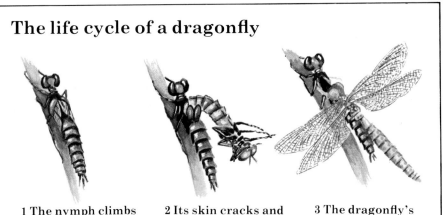

1 The nymph climbs a plant stem.

2 Its skin cracks and the adult emerges.

3 The dragonfly's wings expand.

Dragonfly eggs hatch into nymphs, without wings. The nymph lives underwater for up to four years. Then it climbs out of the water.

The nymph's skin bursts and an adult dragonfly emerges. Its wings expand and stiffen, then it flies off. It will live for about a month.

▲ **Great grey slug** 15cm
This common slug lives in damp places and is active at night or in wet weather. It eats plants or dead animals, and can 'smell' food with its tentacles. It lays eggs which hatch into tiny slugs.

▲ **Common gnat** 7mm
This is a mosquito, often seen near stagnant water. It lays its eggs in raft-like batches on the water surface. The larvae and pupae both hang head downwards from the surface, breathing through tubes.

▲ **Alderfly** 10mm
Usually seen resting in large numbers on waterside plants in early summer. It sits with its wings folded like a roof. The larvae live underwater for up to two years, but the adults only live for about three weeks.

▲ **Drone-fly** 15–19mm
A common hover-fly, which looks like a honey-bee but does not sting. It flies in a series of quick darts. The larva, which lives in water, is called a rat-tailed maggot, because of its long breathing tube.

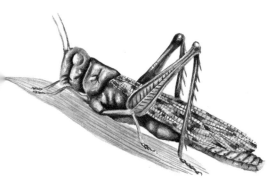

▲ **Common grasshopper** 25mm
Found in grassy places, especially during the summer, when the male chirps. It eats mainly grass. In autumn the female lays eggs in pods. The nymphs hatch in spring, looking like tiny wingless adults.

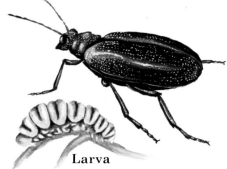

Larva

▲ **Reed beetle** 8mm
Also called a 'living jewel' because of its shiny colour. The larvae live underwater and breathe air trapped in reed stems. The adults can be seen in summer, running over water plants or flying.

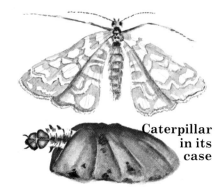

Caterpillar in its case

▲ **China mark moth** 15mm
Seen after dark near stagnant or slow-flowing water. It lays eggs under the leaves of floating plants. The caterpillar makes a floating shelter from oval pieces of leaf, and feeds on the leaves of water plants.

A river bank

The bank is the place where land and water meet, and is full of life.

The soil is soft and damp, ideal for many different plants. Voles and mink tunnel into the soft soil to make their burrows.

Many birds find their food in the water, but nest on the bank.

▼ Alder

This tree is often planted to protect banks from being washed away, because its long roots help to bind the soil together. In spring it has catkins. By autumn these have become brown cones, which contain seeds.

Female flowers

Male catkins

Cones

Young male catkins

▶ A **grey heron** (22) stands in the reeds waiting to spot a fish or frog. It will stand like this for a long time, so one leg is tucked up to keep it warm.

When it sees a fish, the heron will spear it and swallow it whole.

▶ **Trees** which grow near water are often pollinated by the wind and have catkins to help spread their pollen.

Aspens (1) have thick yellow male catkins and green female ones. In early summer the female catkins turn white and fluffy.

Seedhead

A floating seedpod

▲ Yellow flag or iris

A tall plant which grows in damp meadows and beside ponds. The beautiful yellow flowers become flat brown seedpods, which drop into the water when ripe. They float away and grow into new plants further along the bank.

◄ A male **reed bunting** (9) sits on the fluffy seedhead of a **bulrush** (12). It eats tiny insects and seeds. Its nest is hidden in a tussock of reeds. If it is threatened the reed bunting will pretend to be hurt and lead the intruder away.

▼ **Ragged robin**
A tall, reddish plant which grows in damp meadows and marshes, and is called 'ragged' because of its untidy-looking petals.

People once thought it unlucky to take the flowers indoors.

◄ The **kingfisher** (13) has just caught a fish and banged it on the perch to kill it. The fish will be swallowed head first.

In the bank below is the kingfisher's nest, at the end of a tunnel. It is lined with fishbones, and contains six round white eggs.

► **Life cycle of the common frog**
Masses of frogspawn (**1**) are laid in early spring. The tadpoles (**2**) hatch three weeks later.

Gradually they grow legs and lose their tails and gills (**3**). In midsummer tiny frogs with lungs (**4**) jump on to the bank.

Plants on the bank

The soft, damp soil of the bank means that many different plants grow there.

Sedges and reeds often grow at the edge. Plants which grow further up the bank often have large leaves and brightly coloured flowers, like marsh marigolds.

*Not to scale. The height of upright plants is given.

▲ **White willow** 20m
This is one of the commonest willows. Its leaves are silvery-white underneath, so that the tree looks whitish when blown by the wind. In spring it has furry catkins, which grow before the leaves.

▲ **Meadowsweet** 150cm
A tall, leafy plant which often grows in clumps beside rivers and streams. In summer it has frothy clusters of tiny, sweet-scented flowers, each with five petals. It was once spread on floors to perfume rooms.

▲ **Great willowherb** 200cm
There are many willowherbs, and this is one of the largest. It grows on banks and has deep pink flowers in summer. These turn into long thin seedpods. When ripe they split, and the fluffy seeds are blown away.

▲ **Butterbur** 25cm
A low, spreading plant, found in damp meadows and near streams. The leaves can be up to 100cm wide. In late spring it has pink flowers which are clustered on a short, upright stem. Bees love this sweet-scented plant.

▲ **Purple loosestrife** 100–160cm
A tall, upright plant with a stiff hairy stem, and long narrow leaves. In summer it has tall spikes of bright rosy-purple flowers. It often grows in clumps on damp ground beside lakes, rivers and canals.

▲ **Balsam** 120cm
This is one of the balsams found on riverbanks. All of them have seedpods which explode when touched. Another name for this plant is Touch-me-not. Himalayan balsam has purple flowers and is taller.

▲ **Water speedwell** 15-45cm
A low, branching plant which grows at the edge of ponds and streams. In summer it has tall spikes of blue flowers. Each flower has four petals, which fall off easily when shaken by the wind or touched.

▲ **Water forget-me-not** 15-45cm
One of many species of forget-me-not. It grows in shady wet places, and spreads by sending out runners along the ground. These root where they touch earth.

46

Scattering seeds

Plants scatter their seeds so that the new plants will have room to grow.

1 Agrimony   2 Willowherb   3 Cranesbill   4 Burdock

Agrimony (**1**) and burdock (**4**) have hooked seeds. They catch in animal fur and are carried away. Willowherb seeds (**2**) have hairy plumes, and float on the wind. The cranesbill fruit (**3**) explodes, shooting out the seeds.

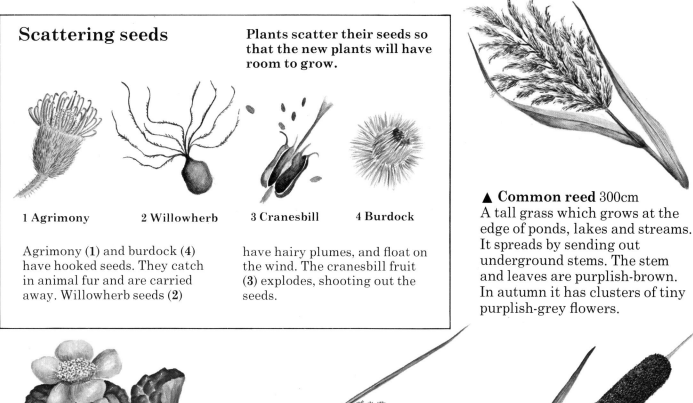

▲ **Common reed** 300cm
A tall grass which grows at the edge of ponds, lakes and streams. It spreads by sending out underground stems. The stem and leaves are purplish-brown. In autumn it has clusters of tiny purplish-grey flowers.

▲ **Marsh marigold** 45cm
An early-flowering plant, seen on marshy ground and river banks in early spring. Clusters of yellow flowers contrast with the glossy green leaves, and then become round green seedpods. It is also called a kingcup.

▲ **Soft rush** 100-200cm
There are many kinds of rush. All are grass-like plants with long, narrow leaves, tall stems filled with pith, and greenish-brown flowers. Soft rush grows in damp meadows and near water, often forming tussocks.

▲ **Reedmace** 100–200cm
Often wrongly called a bulrush, the reedmace grows at the edge of ponds, lakes and streams, and is easily recognized by its tall brown seedhead. This bursts in spring, shedding the fluffy seeds to be blown away.

▲ **Branched bur-reed** 120cm
This sturdy plant grows near rivers and ponds. It has stiff, three-sided leaves and round flower-heads. The fruits are yellow-brown nuts which vary in shape. Some are round, others boat-shaped.

▲ **Common sedge** 200cm
There are many different sedges. All grow near water and in wet meadows. The stems are three-sided, and it has flat narrow, greyish leaves, which roll up when dry. The tiny greenish flowers grow in spikes.

▲ **Great pond sedge** 100–150cm
Usually found near ponds, lakes and slow-flowing streams or canals. It has thin green leaves. In autumn it grows a tall flower spike. The male flowers are clustered on a thin spike above the fatter female spike.

Animals that live near water

Many different animals live on the bank. As well as birds and invertebrates there are mammals, like otters, amphibians, like frogs, and reptiles, like snakes.

Mammals and reptiles breed on land but eat water plants or animals. Amphibians breed in water, but spend most of their lives on land.

*Not to scale. The size given is the body-length of a mature adult.

▲ **Muskrat** 26–40cm, tail 19–27cm
A large vole from North America, which lives in parts of Europe but not in Britain since 1937. It builds a lodge in shallow water and is a good swimmer and diver. It is nocturnal, and lives mainly on plants.

▲ **Water shrew** 76–96mm, tail 52–72mm
This tiny animal lives in a burrow near slow streams and in marshes. It swims and dives for short periods, and eats frogs, worms, insects and small fish. The owl is its chief enemy.

▲ **Coypu** 60cm
A large rodent, which is often mistaken for an otter. It escaped from fur farms in the 1930s. It eats plants and is active at night. Its burrowing can damage river banks and make them collapse.

▲ **Otter** 1.2m
A secretive, nocturnal mammal, which rests during the day in its holt, often a hole in a river bank. At night it hunts many different animals including frogs, fishes, moorhens, crayfish and water voles.

▲ **Water vole** 19–21cm, tail 11cm
Often confused with the brown rat, which also swims well. The water vole eats mainly bank plants. It lives in a burrow in the bank, and is very short-sighted. Many animals eat water voles.

▲ **Mink** 30-43cm, tail 13–23cm
This American relative of the weasel escaped from fur farms and now lives by many rivers, often in disused water vole burrows. It is nocturnal and swims well. Mink eat poultry as well as water animals.

▲ Fire-bellied toad 4–5cm
This brightly-coloured amphibian is found in parts of Europe but not in Britain. It lives in streams and ponds. If any enemy threatens it the toad will stand on its hind legs and display its red-blotched underside.

Eggs, laid singly on water plants

Spawn

▲ Common toad 6–10cm
Toads return to the water where they were hatched to breed. The female lays long strings of eggs which are twisted round water plants.
At night toads hunt tiny animals such as worms.

▲ Fire salamander 30cm
Found in parts of Europe but not in Britain. It is a close relative of the newt, but gives birth to live young. They live in water for about four months, then spend the rest of their lives on land, in damp areas.

▲ Grass snake 60–100cm
Found throughout western Europe but not in Ireland, where there are no snakes. It lives near water and eats frogs, toads, newts and fish. In winter it hibernates in a hole. Young snakes hatch from eggs.

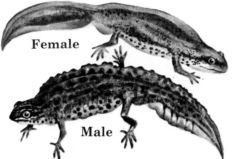

Female

Male

▲ Smooth newt 10cm
An amphibian, which lives mainly on land. At night it hunts for slugs, snails and insects. Its skin is dry and roughish. When it returns to water to breed, the male grows a crest and becomes more brightly coloured.

Male

Female

▲ Great crested newt 14–16cm
The largest European newt. It lives in fairly deep ponds and hibernates on land. In the breeding season the male grows a high ragged crest along his back and tail. When seized this newt gives out a nasty fluid.

▲ Daubenton's bat 8cm, wingspan 25cm
A small bat, also called the water bat. It can be seen flying before dusk, over streams, ponds and rivers, catching flying insects. It hibernates in hollow trees, hanging upside-down.

Animal footprints

You may see these in mud or snow. Hind foot (H) on left, fore foot (F) on right.

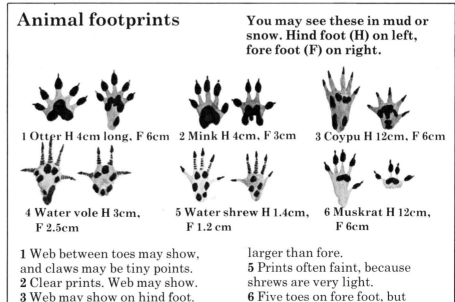

1 Otter H 4cm long, F 6cm   2 Mink H 4cm, F 3cm   3 Coypu H 12cm, F 6cm

4 Water vole H 3cm, F 2.5cm   5 Water shrew H 1.4cm, F 1.2 cm   6 Muskrat H 12cm, F 6cm

1 Web between toes may show, and claws may be tiny points.
2 Clear prints. Web may show.
3 Web may show on hind foot.
4 Star-shaped prints. Hind foot larger than fore.
5 Prints often faint, because shrews are very light.
6 Five toes on fore foot, but usually only four show.

A pond

Life in a pond is rich and varied. The water is still and warm. Plants grow easily in the muddy bottom, and give shelter to animals.

The plants and animals are linked in foodchains. All eat and all are eaten. This balance can be upset if the pond becomes polluted.

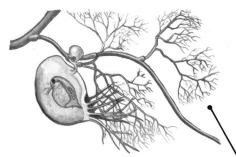

▲ Bladderwort

This is an insect-eating water plant, without roots. On its leaves there are tiny air-filled bladders which trap animals such as water fleas.

In winter, buds drop off. They grow into new plants in spring.

▲ Water spider

This is the only spider which lives under water all the time. Its web is filled with air, which it brings down from the surface. The spider leaves the bell to hunt water fleas and other small animals.

► Caddis flies

Caddis flies live near ponds and ditches, and fly at night. The larvae protect their soft bodies by making tubes out of sand, shell, pieces of leaf or twigs. They sieve tiny food particles from the water.

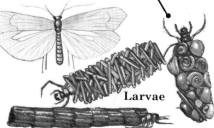

Adult

Larvae

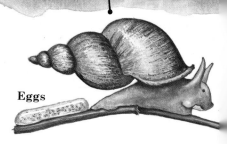

Eggs

Nymph

5

6

◄ Dragonfly and nymph
The young dragonfly is called a nymph. It lives underwater and breathes through gills.

Both the adult and the nymph are fierce hunters. The nymph catches insects, tadpoles and small fish with its 'mask'. This is its hooked bottom jaw, which it can shoot out quickly.

▼ Yellow water-lily
The rounded flowers are smaller than those of the white water-lily. It is also called brandy-bottle because of the shape of its seedpods.

The leaves and flowers float on the surface of the water because their stems are filled with air-spaces.

8

10

46

12

16

17

15

23

21

22

13

▼ Spotted gnat
A mosquito, which sits on the water with its body tilted upwards. The female lays single eggs which float until they hatch.

The larva swims and feeds on tiny animals. It lies along the surface of the water to breathe. The common gnat larva hangs head downwards and breathes through its tail.

32

33

45

44

Larva

39

41

43

42

40

◄ Great pond snail
A common snail, which lays eggs in long strings of jelly on plants or stones. Tiny snails hatch from the eggs after three or four weeks. Many of them are eaten by other snails, fishes and birds.

Key	15 Damselfly	31 Water fleas
	16 Common frog	32 Carp
1 Marsh marigold	17 Minnow	33 Water crowfoot
2 Rush	18 Water boatman	34 Caddis-fly larva
3 Reedmace	19 Whirligig beetles	35 Hornwort
4 Bulrush	20 Saucer bugs	36 Canadian pondweed
5 Yellow flag	21 Frogbit	37 Tench
6 Sedge	22 Pondskater	38 Broad-leaved pondweed
7 Moorhen	23 Spotted gnat	39 Mites
8 Coot	24 Duckweed	40 Swan mussel
9 Swallow	25 Bladderwort	41 Three-spined stickleback
10 Dragonfly	26 Great diving beetle	42 Sponge
11 Mayfly	27 Common newt	43 Dragonfly nymph
12 Water plantain	28 Snail eggs	44 Spiked water milfoil
13 Arrowhead	29 Water spider	45 Freshwater shrimp
14 Rudd	30 Great pond snail	46 Yellow water-lily

Tiny animals in the water

Some water invertebrates, like pondskaters, live on top of the water. Some, like snails, live under the water but have to return to the surface for air. They live in shallow water. Some, like leeches, use dissolved oxygen, and live in deeper water.

*Not to scale. The size given is the body-length of a mature adult.

▲ **Water scorpion** 1–2cm
The long 'tail' is a breathing tube, not a sting. This bug lives in shallow weedy water, and is a bad swimmer. It catches insects, tadpoles and small fishes with its front legs, and sucks out their juices with its beak.

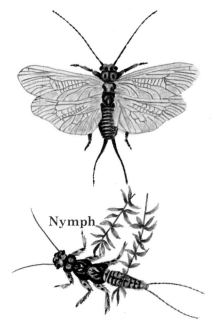

Nymph

▲ **Stonefly** 6–12mm
The nymphs live underwater for up to three years, but the adults live for only two to three weeks. They have two pairs of wings, which are folded flat when resting. Although they can fly, they are usually seen hiding under stones near fast-flowing water.

▲ **Pondskater** 14–17mm
This long-legged bug skims over the surface of ponds and lakes. It rows with its middle legs and steers with its hind legs, held up by the surface tension. It sucks the juices from small insects such as water fleas.

▲ **Water stick insect** 30–35mm
Like the water scorpion, this bug has a long breathing tube and lives near the edges of still water. Its eggs also have breathing tubes.

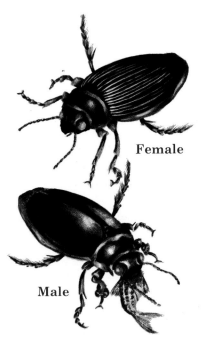

Female

Male

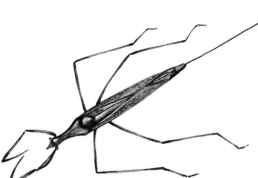

▲ **Water measurer** 8–12mm
This bug walks slowly on the surface of still water in ponds and ditches. It stabs tiny animals, such as water fleas, with its sharp beak. In winter it rests under a stone on land.

▲ **Backswimmer** 15mm
This lively bug swims on its back, using its fringed legs to propel it through the water. It hunts tadpoles and beetle larvae. Air from the surface is trapped in the hairs covering its body, making it look silver.

▲ **Great diving beetle** 35mm
A fierce hunter, found in ponds. It breathes by floating to the surface tail first and letting air flow under its wingcases. The larvae have huge pincers and will attack anything from other beetles to small fishes.

▲ **Whirligig beetle** 5–6mm
A tiny black beetle, often seen in groups. It swims in circles on the surface of ponds with its back out of the water. It can dive underwater, carrying an air bubble. Its larvae live on the bottom, and have gills.

Breathing underwater

These are four different ways of taking in oxygen from the surface.

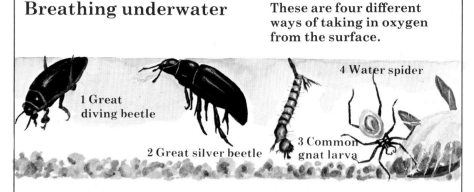

1 Great diving beetle

2 Great silver beetle

3 Common gnat larva

4 Water spider

The great diving beetle (1) takes in air at its hind end. The great silver beetle (2) breaks the surface with one of its antennae. Both store the air under their wingcases. The gnat larva (3) breathes through a tube. The water spider (4) stores air in its underwater web.

▲ **Great silver beetle** 40mm
This beetle eats mainly plants. To breathe it rises to the surface and breaks the surface tension with one of its antennae, so that air can flow under its wingcases. The trapped air makes it look silver when it dives.

▲ **Great pond snail** 5–6cm
Very common in ponds and weedy lakes. It feeds on algae and dead animals. Its eggs are laid in a jelly capsule holding up to 300 eggs. Each hatches into a tiny snail. An adult can have up to eight whorls on its tall shell.

▲ **Great ramshorn snail** 35mm wide
Unlike other snails the ramshorn has red blood. It lives in ponds, weedy lakes and slow-flowing rivers, eating algae and decaying plants and animals. Its shell is flattened, with five or six whorls.

▲ **Freshwater shrimp** 20mm
Found in large numbers under stones and among plants in most clean streams, ponds and shallow lakes. It swims on its side, and you will often find a female carrying a smaller male. It eats mainly decaying plants, and is eaten by many fishes. The female lays eggs in brood pouches on her legs.

▲ **Horse leech** 15cm
Found in ponds and slow-flowing water. Some leeches suck blood but this one swallows small animals such as worms and insect larvae whole. It has a sucking disc at each end of its body.

▲ **Tubifex worms** 3cm
Colonies of these bright red worms live on the muddy bottoms of slow-flowing streams and rivers. Their waving 'tails' make a current, which brings fresh oxygen to them. If disturbed they draw back into their tubes.

Pollution

What happens to waste?

All animals and plants die. This is part of the natural cycle of life. When they die, their remains sink to the bottom of the water, where tiny organisms, called bacteria, break them down. They become part of the material on the bottom and in the water, which other plants and animals feed on.

Bacteria need oxygen to break down dead plants and animals. If there is too much dead matter all the oxygen will be used up before the bacteria have broken down all the waste. The water will seem to be dead.

However, some bacteria do not need oxygen, and slowly they break down the extra waste. The water becomes clean again.

Chemical pollution

Bacteria cannot clean water which has been polluted by chemicals. The balance of the water is altered.

Some chemicals are poisonous to fish, and kill them directly. The waste which many factories pour into the water often contains poisonous chemicals. Insecticides, sprayed on to crops and then blown into nearby waters, also poison fish.

▼ **How water is polluted**
Rivers are fresh and clean when they start, but may be lifeless by the time they reach the sea.

Pollution is caused by people. These are just five of the ways in which the balance of freshwater life is upset.

▼ **Many farmers spray their fields with chemical fertilizers. The rain washes these into nearby rivers and streams, where they upset the chemical balance of the water. Plants grow too fast and block out the light.**

▼ **The village pond is often used as a rubbish dump. People throw in anything from household waste to old cars, thinking the water will hide everything. The results look terrible, and destroy the life of the pond.**

Other chemicals have an indirect effect. They alter the balance of the water so that plants grow too fast and block out the light. A layer of algae covers the surface, so that no oxygen or light can enter the water. Underwater plants die. There is nothing for small animals, such as insect larvae and water fleas, to eat, so they die. Without food or oxygen larger animals die. The water becomes empty and dead, with an unpleasant smell and scum covering the surface.

This sort of pollution can be caused by chemical fertilizers from fields, or by waste being dumped. Waste may also make the water cloudy, so that plants cannot get light. They die, and so do the animals which eat them.

Destroying habitats

Another form of water pollution is the destruction of the places where plants and animals live – their habitats. Rivers, lakes and reservoirs are often used for water-skiing and pleasure-cruising. The wash from motorboats breaks down the banks, and their engines leave an oily film on the water, blocking out oxygen and light.

What you can do

You can help to stop habitats being destroyed. Think about the animals and plants you see. They have a right to live too. Don't pick wild flowers or dig them up. If you're having a picnic, take your rubbish home or put it in a litter-bin. Though these may seem to be small things, they are very important.

It is easy to destroy a habitat, and impossible to replace it. By destroying the balance of life in fresh waters we are destroying ourselves, for we depend on animals and plants for our food and oxygen.

▼ Factories are often built beside rivers. They use the water in their manufacturing processes and pour poisonous chemical wastes back into the river. These kill freshwater life, and make the river look and smell foul.

▼ Power stations use water in their cooling towers and then return it to the river, when it is warmer than the river water. This makes plants grow too fast. Fish may be killed by the rise in temperature.

▼ Sewage works also use water, running it through sewage to help break it down. This process takes large amounts of oxygen from the water, so that animals cannot live there. It also fills the water with black sludge.

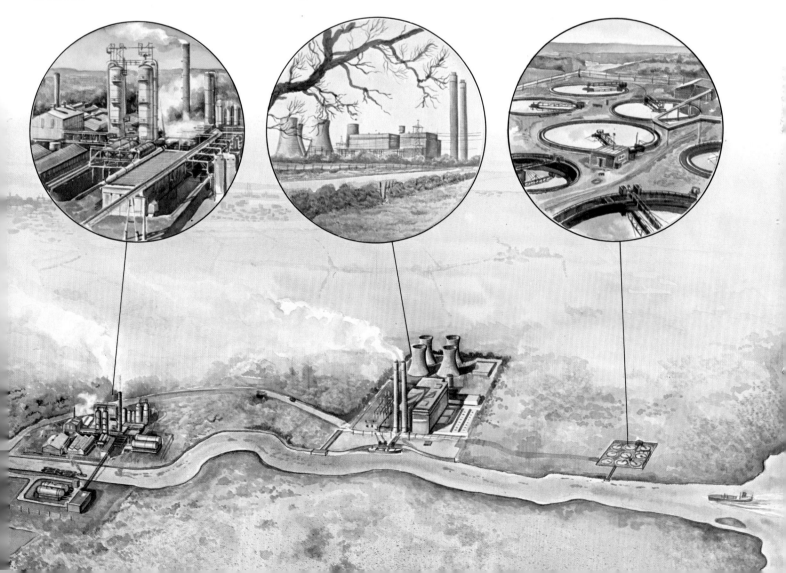

Sandy shores

Sand is easily moved about by the wind and the waves. The surface sand dries up quickly when the tide is out, so there are very few safe places for plants and animals to live.

Burrowing animals

Most sandy shore animals live under the sand. They are protected from the waves, and the sand stays firm and damp, even when the tide is out.

The lugworm (23) lives in a U-shaped burrow. The worm coats the inside of the tube with sticky mucus to stop it from collapsing. It feeds by swallowing sand and digesting the food it contains. The sandy worm-casts are easy to find when the tide is out.

The ragworm (22), more common on muddy shores, also lives in a slime-lined burrow, which it leaves to find food.

Most sea-anemones live on rocks. There are few rocks on sandy shores, but one anemone (17) has overcome the problem by living in a burrow. Only its feeding tentacles lie on the surface, and these are withdrawn into the burrow at any disturbance.

Adult jellyfish

Swimming larva (summer)

Grows attached to a stone (winter)

Divides into discs (spring)

◀ Jellyfish life cycle
The larva (1) attaches itself to a rock. The body grows (2), producing 16 tentacles (3). The body divides into a pile of discs (4). The discs grow tentacles and swim away (5). Each grows into an adult jellyfish.

Feeding tentacles and gills

Shell

Gravel

Sand

Bristle-legs

◀ Sandmason
The sandmason makes its long, delicate, untidy tubes from sand, small stones or bits of shell. It glues the pieces together with slime. The worm moves up and down inside the tube using 17 pairs of bristle-legs.

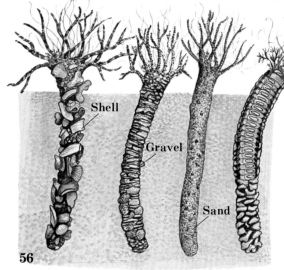

A burrowing fish
The sand-eel (36) burrows into fine, clean sand using its long, extendable jaws. The wet sand keeps the eel moist when the tide is out. It also hides the sand-eel from birds or larger fish looking for a tasty meal.

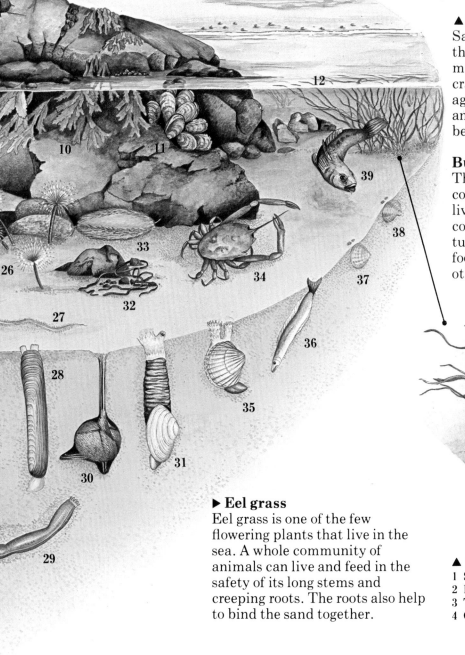

▲Sandhoppers
Sandhoppers are very useful as they eat all kinds of decaying matter – like seaweed and dead crabs. They hop by pushing against the ground with their tails and suddenly straightening their bent bodies.

Buried bivalve molluscs
The razor shell (25), (28), the cockle (35) and sand gaper (31) live buried in the sand. They are connected to the surface by two tubes called 'siphons'. One brings food and water to the body. The other pumps out water and waste.

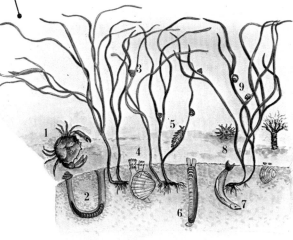

▶ Eel grass
Eel grass is one of the few flowering plants that live in the sea. A whole community of animals can live and feed in the safety of its long stems and creeping roots. The roots also help to bind the sand together.

Starfishes, sea-urchins, sea-anemones

Starfishes and sea-urchins belong to the Echinoderms ('spiny-skinned'). They have chalky plates under the skin, and move on tube-feet.

Sea-anemones have no skeletons. Their bodies have a sucker at the bottom.

* Not to scale. Average size given.

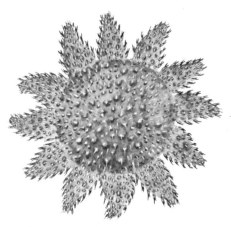

▲**Cushion star** 2-4cm diameter
This small browny-yellow or green starfish is found under stones on the lower shore. Its rough, stiff body has five short arms with rounded tips, and looks rather like an old-fashioned pincushion.

▲**Common sunstar** 15-25cm diameter
The sunstars live in the sea but may be washed up. They have from ten to fourteen blunt-ended arms. This one looks like a flaming sun. It feeds on oysters, mussels and other starfish.

▲**Common starfish** 10-50cm diameter
Often found on the lower shore in mud, sand and rocky pools. Its colour varies from brownish-yellow to purple. It eats mussels and oysters, which it pulls open with its tube-feet.

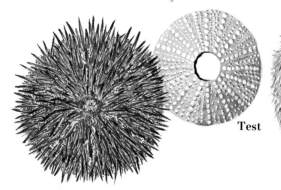

Test

Test

▲**Green sea-urchin** 5-6cm
This prickly animal lives on the lower shore. Its green spines have purple tips. It disguises itself with pieces of seaweed or small stones which stick on to the spines. The empty shell, called a **test**, is also green.

▲**Sea-potato** 10cm
A common sea-urchin, which burrows to a depth of 15cm in clean sand. It often lives in groups in the middle and lower shore. The test looks like a potato.

▲**Common brittle-star** 12cm diameter (top) **Burrowing brittle-star** up to 30cm diameter (bottom)
Common on the lower shore of sandy beaches or among rocks. The burrowing brittle-star has very long arms and burrows in the sand. Look for the five rows of spines on the common brittle-star. The arms are easily broken but will slowly regrow.

58

▲ **Dead men's fingers** 20cm high
These animals are halfway
between anemones and corals.
Each of the flesh-coloured
branches contains many
anemone-like animals. They have
jellyish bodies, which are held up
by chalky rods.

▲ **Snakelocks anemone** 10cm
high
Lives in shallow, sunny rock pools
on the middle and lower shore. It
is a dull green-brown, and has 200
purple-tipped tentacles. They
wave about like tiny snakes, and
cannot be completely withdrawn.

Sea-anemones

Beadlet anemones are very
common on rocks and in pools
on rocky shores. There are red,
green and strawberry forms, all
with 24 bright blue spots at the
top of the body. Their stinging
tentacles can poison even a
small fish.

Out of water, sea-anemones look
like blobs of jelly. They pull in
their tentacles and trap water to
stop them drying up.

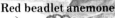

Sea-anemone
out of water

Strawberry
beadlet
anemone

Red beadlet anemone

Sea-anemone
catching a fish

▲ **Dahlia anemone** 15cm high
This large anemone hides among
the rocks, stones and weeds in the
middle and lower shore pools. It
often attaches bits of shell, gravel
or weed to the sticky grey warts on
its body for camouflage.

▲ **Daisy anemone** 10cm high
This trumpet-shaped anemone
lives in rocky crevices or buried in
mud on the lower shore. It
withdraws out of sight if
disturbed. There are about 750
short, spotted tentacles.

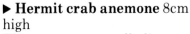

▶ **Hermit crab anemone** 8cm
high
This anemone usually lives on the
shells of large hermit crabs,
although it can live on rocks. It
eats scraps of food left by the crab.
The anemone protects the crab
with its stinging tentacles.

▲ **Burrowing anemone** 10cm
high
This worm-like anemone burrows
in sand and mud for protection.
The body has 12 stripes running
from top to bottom. There are 12
pointed tentacles, with arrow-
shaped marks at their bases.

59

Worms and jellyfishes

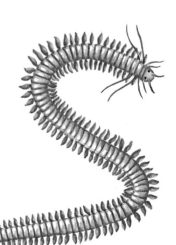

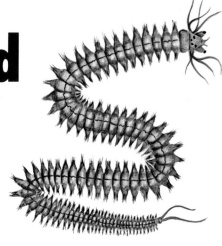

There are many fascinating seashore animals hiding on a beach. Burrowing worms are easy to find. Look for worm-casts on sand and mud. These show the positions of their burrows. Sponges and tube-worms are common on the lower parts of the shore.

Jellyfishes are often stranded on the beach as the tide goes out. You may also find hornwrack and sea-mat left behind by the tide.

* Not to scale. Average body length given.

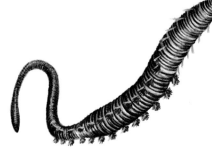

▲ **Lugworm** 20cm
A common worm which lives in U-shaped burrows in sand and mud, from the middle shore downwards. The soft, plump body has red feathery gills. Fishermen dig lugworms up for bait.

▲ **Ragworm** 12cm
A common worm which burrows in sand and mud in the middle and lower shores. Its colour varies from orange to green. Look for the red blood-vessel running down its back. It has over 100 bristly segments.

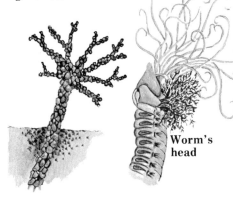

Worm's head

▲ **Sandmason** 30cm
You may see tiny tubes sticking out of the sand or mud at low tide. Some are the homes of sandmasons. These worms build fragile tubes out of tiny grains of sand, gravel, or shell, stuck together with slime.

▲ **Green leaf worm** 5-15cm
This bright green worm is common in rock pools in the middle and lower shore. It swims about, using its large bristles as paddles. At low tide it creeps over rocks, feeding on barnacles.

▲ **Peacock worm** 25cm
The brightly coloured peacock worm also lives in a tube. When covered by water the animal moves up its tube and strains food from the water with its gills. At low tide the tube traps water, so the worm can keep wet.

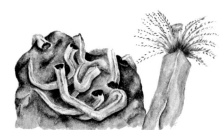

▲ **Keelworm** 2.5cm tube 5-6cm
These common worms make twisting chalky tubes on rocks and shells. On the top is a ridge or 'keel'. When it is underwater, the worm puts out a crown of red and white gills, with which it catches food.

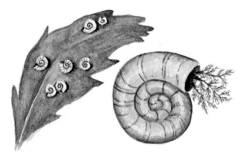

▲ **Spirorbis** diameter 35mm
A worm which lives in tiny chalky tubes on the fronds of brown seaweeds, oarweeds, rocks and stones. When the tide is out, the worm closes the end of the tube with a tiny chalky flap to trap water inside.

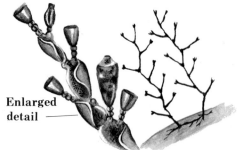

Enlarged detail

▲ **Obelia** 4cm high
Found on brown seaweeds and oarweeds. The tiny zigzag stems look like plants, but each branch contains a tiny, anemone-like animal. The upright 'stems' are connected by creeping root-like tubes.

▲ Sea-mouse 10-20cm
This strange, flat, oval-shaped worm is covered with fine hairs which are brilliant green and gold. It usually lives offshore but may be found in lower shore pools. Sea-mice are often washed up on the beach.

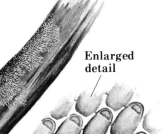

Enlarged detail

▲ Sea-mat
You may see small whitish patches on brown seaweeds and oarweed. With a hand lens you will see that each is made of tiny white boxes. Each box contains a minute animal, living inside a chalky 'shell'.

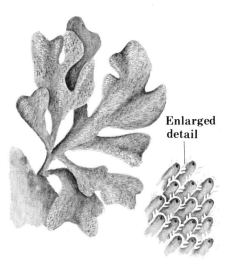

Enlarged detail

▲ Hornwrack 20cm
Like the sea-mat this is a group of animals, each living in a tiny chalky box. Colonies form a shape like a flat plant. They live in deep water, but when dead are often washed up on beaches.

▲ Common jellyfish diameter 25cm
This common animal floats in shallow sheltered water like a transparent umbrella. On top are four violet, horseshoe-shaped marks (its reproductive organs), and four mouth arms hang below.

▲ Stalked jellyfish 5cm high
A tiny trumpet-shaped jellyfish with eight bunches of knob-like tentacles around the edge of its body. It usually stays in one place, attached to seaweeds in pools on the lower shore, but sometimes swims or floats.

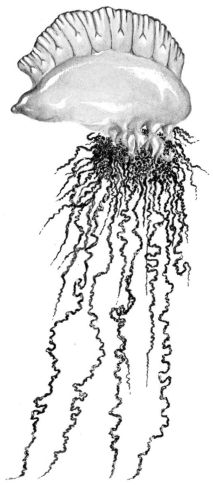

▲ Portuguese man-o'-war 15-30cm
This jellyfish has a gas-filled bladder which floats. Long tentacles trail underneath, catching food. Some have dangerous stinging cells.

Sponges

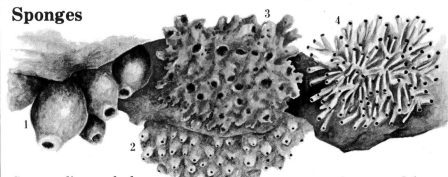

Sponges live on the lower shore. They are colonies of single cells inside a soft covering supported by tiny splinters of chalk or silica.

1 Purse sponge: 3-5cm long. Hangs down on the underside of rocks.

2 Breadcrumb sponge: Like a piece of green foam-rubber.

3 Myxilla: A cushion-like sponge on rocks and sometimes on spidercrabs.

4 Leucosolenia: Often attached to seaweeds.

A rock pool

Rock pools come in all shapes and sizes. Each is a tiny world full of fascinating animals and plants. What you find in a rock pool will vary a great deal, depending on its level on the shore.

Keeping wet

To stop drying up, common limpets (2) cling so firmly to the rocks when the tide is out, that their shells cut a groove in the stone. They always return to the same spot on a rock.

The bladder wrack (1) and serrated wrack (4) can survive out of water for several hours. The sea-oak (33), sea-lettuce (22) and peacock's tail (21), however, will quickly dry up and die out of water, so they always live in pools or shallow water.

The common blenny (16) eats barnacles and mussels. It has a smooth body and can slither short distances through weeds and over rocks from one pool to another. The two slug-like sea-lemons (23) are feeding on the breadcrumb sponge (24).

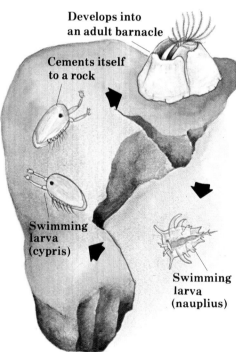

Develops into an adult barnacle

Cements itself to a rock

Swimming larva (cypris)

Swimming larva (nauplius)

▲ Barnacle life cycle

The eggs hatch into tiny swimming larvae (1). Each larva grows extra segments, eyes and mouthparts. After three weeks it changes into a two-shelled larva (2) and looks for a home. It cements itself on to a rock (3) and grows into an adult barnacle (4).

▼ Dogwhelks

Dogwhelks are carnivores. They have long drill-like mouthparts, with which they bore holes in the shells of mussels or barnacles, and suck out the contents. Dirty-white dogwhelks have eaten only barnacles (1). Those that only eat mussels are darker (2). Stripey dogwhelks have had a mixed diet (3).

Key

1	Bladder wrack
2	Limpets
3	Periwinkles
4	Serrated wrack
5	Dogwhelks
6	Barnacles
7	Enteromorpha
8	Springtails
9	Mussels
10	Sea-belt
11	Prawn
12	Cystoseira
13	Brittle-star
14	Pod weed
15	Shore crab
16	Blenny
17	Chiton
18	Topshells
19	Snakelocks anemone
20	Beadlet anemone
21	Peacock's tail
22	Sea-lettuce
23	Sea-lemon
24	Breadcrumb sponge
25	Common starfish
26	Green sea-urchin
27	Oyster
28	Cushion star
29	Hermit crab
30	Hermit crab anemone
31	Pea crab
32	Coral weed
33	Sea oak

Feeding habits

The tentacles of the snakelocks anemone (19) wave gently in the water. If the small prawn (11) touches them, it will be paralysed. The tentacles will then guide the food into the anemone's mouth, in the middle of the tentacles.

The hermit crab anemone (30) lives on the hermit crab's whelk shell (29). The anemone helps to disguise the crab. In return it eats food scraps left by the crab.

The barnacles (6) are busy feeding. Their six feathery legs kick in and out, straining tiny particles of food from the water.

◀ Life on a holdfast

Many seaweeds are attached to rocks by leathery, root-like structures called **holdfasts.**

Several animals live in this oarweed holdfast. It shelters them against waves, hides them from enemies and stops them from drying up.

◀ Key

1	Stalked jellyfish	4	**Blue-rayed limpet**
2	**Beadlet anemone**	5	**Shore crab**
3	**Sea squirt**	6	**Mussels**
		7	**Keelworms**

▼ Springtails

The springtail is one of the few insects found on the beach. Look for it on the surface of sea-water trapped in small, rocky hollows. Large groups of them float round and round, looking like patches of blue-black velvet.

▼ Pea crab

The tiny, almost transparent pea crab lives inside the shells of living molluscs, such as mussels, oysters and cockles. The crab keeps the mollusc clean by eating scraps of food from its gills.

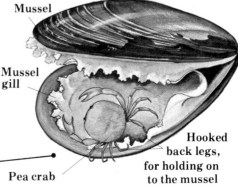

Mussel

Mussel gill

Pea crab

Hooked back legs, for holding on to the mussel

Molluscs

Molluscs are mostly small, slow-moving animals with gills and a chalky shell. They are found everywhere on the shore, at different levels, depending on how long they can live out of water, uncovered by the tide.

Some are like the slugs and snails that live on land. Others, called bivalves, have two hinged shells. They burrow in mud and sand, and sometimes in wood and rock. The octopus is a mollusc, although its shell is inside its body.

* Not to scale. The average length of body is given.

How a razor shell burrows

1 The muscular foot wriggles into the sand. It is hatchet-shaped, so that it cannot easily be pulled out of the sand.
2 The foot contracts, pulling the shell upright.

3 The foot wriggles deeper into the sand. When it contracts again, the shell is pulled further down.
4 The razor shell can bury itself very quickly. Water, containing food and oxygen, is taken to and from the body through special tubes called siphons.

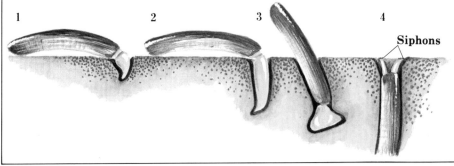

Siphons

▲Periwinkles: Edible 2.5cm high (left) Flat 1cm high (right) There are several different kinds of these common, snail-like molluscs. Each is found at a different level on the shore. They feed on seaweed and vary in colour.

▲Topshells: Painted 2.5cm high (left) Grey 1.25cm high (right) These are the two most common topshells. The grey topshell is flatter and less brightly coloured than the painted topshell, and is very common.

▲Cockle 5cm (left) Tellin 2cm (right) These bivalves burrow in sand and mud in the middle and lower shore. With its long siphons, the cockle sifts food from the sand. The tellin sucks food from the surface of the sand.

▲Common limpet 7cm Limpets are snails with cone-shaped shells, and are found on rocky shores. They feed on seaweeds, using a rasping tongue. They stick firmly to a rock when the tide goes out, and trap water inside their shells.

▲ Blue-rayed limpet 2cm This beautiful animal lives on oarweeds. It is common on rocky beaches, usually in the lower shore zone. Its shell is smooth, and almost transparent, with several rows of bright blue spots. These become duller with age.

▲Chiton 2cm The shell of this small, shield-shaped mollusc is made up of eight overlapping plates. It is sometimes called a 'coat-of-mail' shell and can curl up, like a woodlouse. Small numbers of chitons can be found under rocks.

▲ **Queen scallop** 9cm
An edible bivalve which lives offshore, usually on sand. It can swim away from danger, such as a starfish, by clapping its shells together. Single shells are often washed up by the tide.

▲ **Pelican's foot shell** 3.5cm
You may find this unusual shell washed up on the beach. When alive it lives in deep water, where it burrows in mud and sand. Its name comes from the 'wing' on the shell, which looks like a pelican's foot.

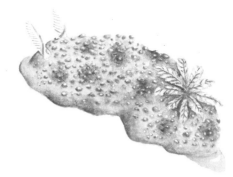

▲ **Sea-lemon** 7cm
This slug-like mollusc has no shell. Its yellowish body looks rather like a piece of lemon peel. In summer it is sometimes found in rocky pools on the lower shore. Look for the flower-like gills on its back.

▲ **Common mussel** 1-10cm
This very common bivalve attaches itself to rocks by strong 'byssus' threads. It lives on rocky shores, or on stones on muddy shores. You will often find clusters of small mussels in rocky crevices.

▲**Common whelk** 8cm high
The common or edible whelk lives in the sea, where it feeds on seaweeds and other molluscs, such as mussels. Empty whelk shells are washed ashore, and often become homes for hermit crabs.

▲ **Dogwhelk** 3cm high
Dogwhelks are smaller than common whelks. They are also carnivores, and eat mussels and barnacles, using a rasping tongue. The colour of dogwhelks depends on their diet. They live on the middle shore.

▲ **Portuguese oyster** 15cm wide
This oyster came originally from the Bay of Biscay and was grown in oyster beds for food. It now also lives in estuaries attached to small stones and shells. Amazingly, it is male one year and female the next!

▶ **Lesser octopus** up to 50cm
An uncommon mollusc, with eight arms, each with a row of suckers. It lurks among rocks on the lowest part of the shore. It has well developed eyes and can change colour to match its background.

The crab family

Crabs, shrimps, prawns and lobsters are all crustaceans. They are relatives of the insects and spiders, and have many jointed legs. They usually have a heavy, hard outer skeleton, which makes many crustaceans slow movers. They come in all shapes and sizes, and nearly all live in or near water.

* Not to scale. The average length is given.

▲**Barnacles**
The **goose barnacle** (top) has a long stalk. It lives on floating objects, or on rocks and piers.
▼**Acorn** and **star barnacles** live everywhere on rocks, wood and even other shelled animals. When the tide is out the tiny animal hides inside the hard chalky plates. Water and air are trapped inside. When the tide returns six pairs of feathery legs beat in and out, trapping food.

Acorn barnacle (left): has a diamond-shaped opening, and is found all over the shore.

Star barnacle (right): has a kite-shaped opening, and lives in middle and upper shore zones.

▲ **Common shore crab** 10cm
Very common on the middle and lower parts of most shores, hiding under seaweeds and stones. It can live out of water for quite a long time. It feeds on sandhoppers, molluscs and animal remains.

▲ **Velvet swimming crab** 5-10cm
A beautiful, but very fierce, lower-shore crab. The last part of the back legs is flat, and is used as a paddle when swimming. Look for the hairy shell, and for the blue marks on its legs and pincers.

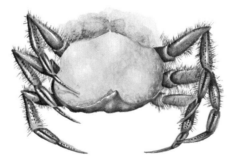

▲ **Parasitic barnacle**
This strange animal lives under the abdomen of shore crabs. It looks like a large yellow leathery sac. These are its reproductive parts. The actual barnacle is underneath, living on the crab's body.

▲ **Edible crab** 5-25cm
You may find this common crab on the middle and lower parts of the shore, under stones and seaweed. Look for the 'piecrust' edge to its pinky-brown shell. It can be cooked and eaten.

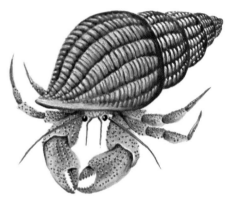

▲ **Common hermit crab** 10cm
Hermit crabs have soft abdomens, so they protect themselves by living in the empty shells of winkles, topshells and whelks. When they have outgrown one shell they find a larger one.

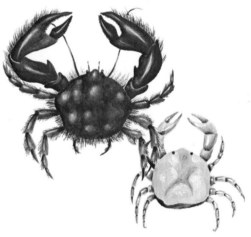

▲ **Broad-clawed porcelain crab** 1.2cm (left)
This is not a true crab. It is common under stones and in mud.

▲ **Pea crab** 1.5cm (right)
Lives inside the shells of living oysters and mussels.

▲Common lobster 45cm
This large, edible crustacean turns red when boiled. It lives among rocks and in caves offshore, but is sometimes marooned in large rock pools. Its large powerful pincers can give you a nasty nip.

▲Gribble 4mm
This tiny crustacean is common in wooden breakwaters or floating timber, where it bores into the wood. In large numbers gribbles cause serious damage. Pieces of gribble-bored wood are often washed up on beaches.

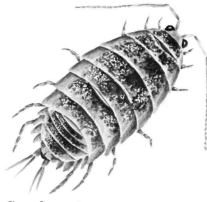

▲Common shrimp 5cm
Shrimps live in sandy shore pools, shallow water and estuaries, usually in large numbers. They are not transparent, like prawns. They burrow in the sand, and feed on ragworms and small crustaceans.

▲Common prawn 5-10cm
Prawns are very common in rocky and sandy pools on the middle and lower shore. They hide under weed, and their almost transparent bodies are difficult to spot as they dart about. This species is edible.

▲Sea slater 2cm
A common splash-zone crustacean which lives under stones and weeds. It is also common in cracks in harbour walls. It hides during the day, only coming out at night to feed on brown seaweeds.

▲Sandhopper 1.5cm
Found in large numbers on the upper shore, where they burrow in the sand and amongst their food: rotting seaweed and dead animal remains. When disturbed, they leap in all directions. They cannot live underwater for very long.

How a prawn moults

Crustaceans, like this prawn, are supported by a stiff outer shell, not an internal skeleton. The shell does not grow, so as the animal grows it has to shed its shell. This is called *moulting*. The shell splits, and the animal wriggles out (left). A soft, larger shell has already developed. This slowly hardens. The animal hides until its new shell is hard.

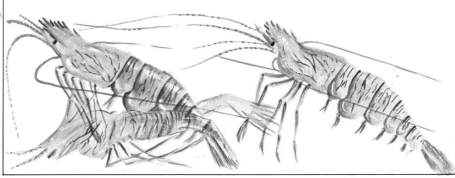

67

Sand dunes

Sand is a difficult habitat to live in. It quickly dries out and is blown about by the wind, so only the toughest plants can survive. Dunes are formed when sand piles up round objects, usually plants.

Key

1	Sea buckthorn	14	Buckshorn plantain	27	Prickly saltwort
2	Ragwort	15	Cat's ear	28	Sea lyme-grass
3	Skylark	16	Creeping thistle	29	Sea rocket
4	Soft rush	17	Sand sedge	30	Marram grass
5	Common reed	18	Daisy	31	Sand couch
6	Broadleaved pondweed	19	Grasshopper	32	Sea bindweed
7	Water mint	20	Snails	33	Sea holly
8	Horsetail	21	Sea campion	34	Sand-wasp
9	Cinnabar moth	22	Black medick	35	Herring gull
10	Ragwort	23	Shepherd's cress	36	Sea sandwort
11	Meadow pipit	24	Sandwich terns	37	Black-headed gull
12	Creeping willow	25	Ladybirds	38	Sea spurge
13	Common tern	26	Bumblebee	39	Painted lady butterfly

Dunes near the beach

Only really tough plants like sea sandwort (36) can grow at the top of the beach. Their thick, fleshy leaves store fresh water and long roots anchor them firmly in the shifting sand.

If an object like a picnic box is left on a windy beach a heap of dry sand will build up around it and soon cover it up. This is how dunes are formed. The long creeping roots of sand couch (31), marram grass (30) and sea lyme-grass (28) bind the sand together. Windblown sand builds up around the plants forming small dunes.

▼ Sand couch

Sand couch lives almost on the beach, and is sometimes covered by the tide. It has spreading underground stems which help to bind the sand together. New shoots sprout on the stems and push up through the sand.

▶ Marram grass

The sand dunes are very dry unless it rains. Marram grass cuts down water loss from its leaves by rolling them up into a tube (1). The outside of this leafy tube is quite waterproof. If it rains the leaf will unroll (2).

Cream and brown **banded snails** are common on sand dunes.

Yellow dunes

Marram grass can grow up through the sand and has long underground roots. Because it lives further from the sea than sand couch, dunes become higher as you move inland. Colonies of common terns (13) may nest here.

Many more plants grow on the sheltered side away from the sea. Sand fescue grass also helps to bind the sand together. You may see sea holly (33), sea campion (21), prickly saltwort (27), sea bindweed (32) and sea rocket (29).

As more plants grow and die, a richer, grey soil is formed.

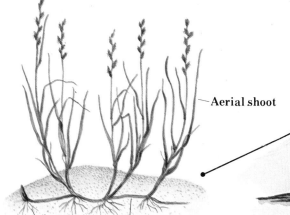

Aerial shoot

Roots   Underground stem

Banded snails

68

Grey dunes

The grey, sandy soil supports plants like black medick (22), cat's ear (15), daisy (18) and buckshorn plantain (14). Their spreading leaves cover the soil. Creeping thistles (16) and sand sedge (17) have long spreading roots which bind the soil.

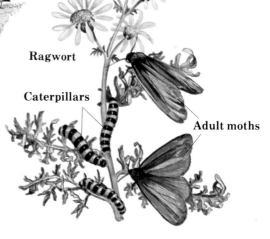

Ragwort

Caterpillars

Adult moths

▼ Sand-wasp

This fierce-looking sand-wasp is carrying a dead caterpillar back to a sandy burrow. The wasp lays an egg on the caterpillar and seals the burrow (1). The wasp larva feeds on the caterpillar (2). The larva turns into a pupa, and then hatches as an adult wasp.

▲ Cinnabar moth

Birds quickly learn not to eat the brightly coloured caterpillars of the cinnabar moth as they have a nasty taste. You may find them in spring feeding on ragwort. The adult moth is also brightly coloured.

Dune slacks

Where dry sand has blown away, a hollow called a slack forms. This fills with rainwater. Creeping willow (12) lives on dunes near these water-filled slacks. Reeds (5), soft rush (4) and water mint (7) also grow here, while caddis flies and mosquitoes breed in the water.

Sea buckthorn (1) grows furthest from the sea. Rabbits can dig their burrows easily in this soft, sandy soil.

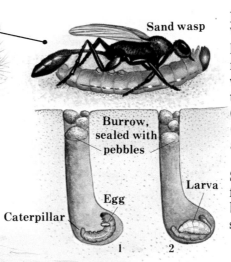

Sand wasp

Burrow, sealed with pebbles

Larva

Egg

Caterpillar

1

2

Beach plants

There are two main groups of plants on the beach. The plants that are covered by the sea are nearly all algae, and are more commonly known as seaweeds. They have no flowers. Above the tide-line, a few tough flowering plants are found. Many have roots which grow deep into the sand and mud.

* Not to scale. The average height is given.

Four common grasses

Most grasses look very alike. To identify them, look at the shape of the flowerheads. These four are common on sand dunes.

1 Cord grass   3 Sand couch
2 Marram grass   4 Sea lyme grass

▲ **Sea sandwort** 20cm
Common on shingle and sandy beaches, where the creeping stems and forked branches often cover quite large areas. The carpet of small fleshy leaves and the spreading roots help to bind the sand together.

▲ **Prickly saltwort** 60cm
An upright or spreading plant found on salt-marshes and sandy beaches. The thick, tough stem has pink or green stripes, and many branches. There are tough prickles at the tips of the fleshy leaves.

▲ **Yellow horned-poppy** 60-80cm
Found growing on sand dunes, shingle and chalky cliffs. In summer, look for the lovely golden yellow flowers up to 8cm across. The seed pods, like curved horns, may be 30cm long. Poisonous.

▲ **Sea rocket** 20-40cm
A straggling, untidy-looking plant with zigzag branches and thick fleshy leaves. It grows near the high-tide mark on sandy beaches and salt-marshes. Clusters of pale mauve flowers appear in summer.

▲ **Sea holly** 50cm
This prickly plant grows on sandy and shingle beaches, in and above the splash zone. The bluish-green, holly-like leaves have white edges. The pale blue flowerheads are also prickly.

▲ **Samphire** 30cm
Sometimes found growing in rocky crevices on the upper shore. The stem and leaves are thick and fleshy, containing water. The leaves are sometimes picked in spring and pickled, like onions.

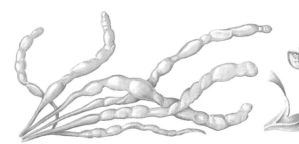

▲ **Enteromorpha** 5-80cm
A very common seaweed, found in most upper shore pools, attached to stones and shells. Its crinkly green fronds are hollow and up to 80cm long. They fill with gas as they grow, and float if broken off.

▲ **Sea-lettuce** 15–50cm
The large, almost transparent fronds look a bit like lettuce leaves. It is very common on the middle and lower shore and in pools on the upper shore, attached to stones and shells.

▲ **Thong weed** Body 5cm, strap up to 200cm
Look for olive-brown, mushroom-like plants on the lower shore. Several long, branched, leathery 'straps' will grow from the dent in the top of each one.

▲ **Lomentaria** 15cm (right)
Lomentaria looks like strings of tiny pink sausages.

▲ **Coral weed** 8cm (left)
The tiny stiff fronds of coral weed have a hard 'skeleton' of lime, like coral.

▲ **Spiral wrack** 60cm (left)
Lives on rocks on the upper shore. The fronds have smooth edges and are often twisted.

▲ **Serrated wrack** 60cm (right)
Lives on the lower shore. It is easy to spot by the toothed, saw-like edge to the fronds.

▶ **Bladder wrack** 15-100cm
Very common on the middle shore. The leathery, strap-like fronds have wavy edges, and many pairs of air-filled bladders.

▲ **Egg wrack** 30-150cm
Very common on sheltered beaches and in estuaries, attached to rocks on the middle shore. The long straggly fronds have air-filled bladders. A small, red, tufted seaweed often grows on egg wrack.

▲ **Irish moss** 7-15cm
A very common seaweed, found on middle and lower parts of rocky shores. Its colour varies from light green to dark red. It has many branches, which make it look rounded. It is also called **carragheen.**

▲**Channelled wrack** 5-15cm
Common on rocks on the upper shore. Look for the groove running down each frond. There are no air bladders, but at the tips of the fronds there are reproductive bodies.

▲ **Oarweed** Up to 300cm
Oarweeds grow low on the shore and are rarely uncovered by the tide. Small plants grow in rock pools. One kind, called sea-belt (left), has long fronds. Another, divided into 'fingers', is called tangleweed (right).

Shore birds

Many different kinds of birds live and feed on the shore. As well as seagulls, there is a large group of birds called waders. They run around at the water's edge, probing the sand or mud for food. Waders are often seen in huge flocks in winter.

* Not to scale. Average body length given.

Birds which feed in mud

The beaks of wading birds are different lengths, so each species feeds on different mud-living animals. For example, **knots** have very short beaks.

They feed on animals which live near the surface, like crabs, worms and small molluscs.
Curlews have very long beaks, which go far into the mud. They can reach deep-burrowing lugworms, ragworms and bivalve molluscs.

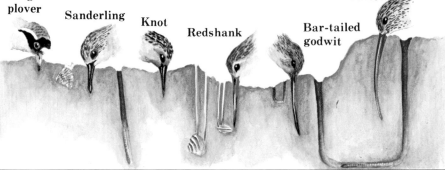

Ringed plover · Sanderling · Knot · Redshank · Bar-tailed godwit · Curlew

▲ **Black-headed gull** 38cm
One of the most common birds on shores, mudflats and estuaries, often in noisy flocks. They breed in colonies on shingle banks, moors and lakes. In summer the head is chocolate brown (not black).

Summer · Winter

▲ **Curlew** 58cm
The largest European wading bird. It is very shy, with a sad call (coor-lee: coor-lee). Curlews are common on mudflats and estuaries. They nest on moors, marshes, meadows and sand-dunes.

▲ **Oystercatcher** 43cm
A very noisy bird, with a 'kleep-kleep' call. It is easy to recognize, with its black upper parts, white underparts and orange beak. It eats oysters, mussels, limpets, crustaceans and worms.

▲ **Ringed plover** 19cm
A small, plump bird, which runs about near the sea, often pausing to search for food. Look for its orange legs and the wide black band across its chest. Large flocks live on sandy and muddy shores.

▲ **Turnstone** 23cm
The speckled feathers help to camouflage the turnstone on stony and muddy beaches. It turns over stones, shells and rubbish with its beak as it searches for food, like mussels, limpets and sandhoppers.

▲**Sanderling** 20cm
Another small, plump, very active wader. When looking for food it races up and down the tideline like a clockwork toy. It spends the winter on sandy beaches, and breeds on stony ground in the Arctic.

▲Dunlin 18cm
Possibly the most common wader, found in huge flocks on estuaries, mudflats, salt-marshes and sandy beaches. In summer it is the only small wader with a black belly. When feeding it looks hunched up.

▶ Redshank 28cm
A noisy, restless wader, which springs into the air at the slightest sign of danger. It gets its name from the colour of its legs. It is a common shore bird, and nests in grassland and marshy places near the sea.

▲Bar-tailed godwit 38cm
This large wader looks like a curlew, but its long beak curves slightly upwards. It gets its name from the stripe of brownish-grey feathers on its white tail. It is very common on estuaries and mudflats.

▲Common tern 35cm
In summer the common tern's beak becomes orange-red with a black tip. You may see terns hovering above the sea looking for fish. They nest in sand dunes and beaches.

▲Little tern 24cm
A very small tern with a black-tipped yellow beak. They tend to hover longer than common terns before diving. They nest in small colonies on sandy and shingly beaches and, in Europe, beside lakes and rivers.

Summer plumage

▲Knot 25cm
Huge flocks of knots can often be seen searching for molluscs and worms on sandy and muddy shores. They all face in the same direction. If disturbed, the flock will take off like a grey cloud.

▲Shelduck 61cm
A large, goose-like duck, which lives on mudflats, estuaries and sandy coasts, and feeds on snails. It sometimes nests in rabbit burrows. You can recognize the male by the knob on its beak.

▲Avocet 43cm
A large, rare wader with an unmistakable beak. It lives on mudflats, estuaries and sand banks. It feeds in shallow water, sifting it with a side-to-side movement of the beak.

Cliffs

The kinds of plants and animals found on cliffs depends on the type of rocks and the amount of soil. Smooth rocks and narrow ledges exposed to hot sun, rain and salt spray are unfriendly places to make a home.

Birds

Birds are the only animals that can reach the cliff ledges easily. Here, noisy colonies of herring gulls (33), razorbills (10) and guillemots (17) will make their nests. The Manx shearwater (5) nests in burrows in the soil on top of the cliff.

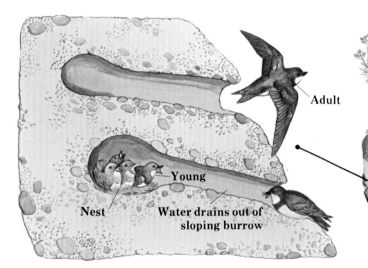

Adult

Young

Nest

Water drains out of sloping burrow

▲ Sand martins

The sand martin nests in colonies in sand and gravel cliffs. Both parents dig a burrow about 1 metre long, and make a nest at the end. The young are fed on insects caught by the parents as they fly. The burrows may be used for several years until they become too full of fleas.

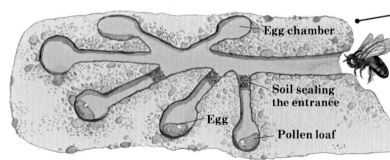

Egg chamber

Soil sealing the entrance

Egg

Pollen loaf

▲ Solitary bees

These insects live in small holes in sandy cliffs. The female digs a burrow in spring. In each chamber, she lays an egg on a tiny loaf of pollen. The larva grows as it eats the pollen. It turns into a pupa and an adult hatches in the summer. The young bees mate and lay eggs. New adults emerge next spring.

Key

1	Blackthorn	12	Fulmar	24 Sand martins
2	Bramble	13	Rock doves	25 Sea campion
3	Rowan	14	Gannet	26 Woodlouse
4	Sycamore	15	Kittiwakes	27 Ladybird
5	Manx shearwater	16	Great black-backed gull	28 Sea storksbill
6	Fennel	17	Guillemots	29 Rove beetle
7	Chough	18	Cormorant	30 Sea milkwort
8	Thyme	19	Golden samphire	31 Scurvy grass
9	Lesser black-backed gull	20	Red valerian	32 Sea pearlwort
10	Razorbill	21	Wild carrot	33 Herring gulls
11	Shags	22	Cliff spurrey	34 Lichens
		23	Sea beet	35 Thrift

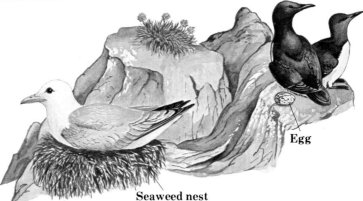

Egg

Seaweed nest

▲ Bird nests

The kittiwake (left) glues its seaweed nest to the rock with mud to stop it from blowing away. Guillemots (right) don't make nests. Each pair lays one egg, which is pear-shaped to stop it rolling off the ledge. The female often holds the egg on her feet to keep it warm.

Plants

At the base of the cliff grow tough, leathery plants like sea beet (23), sea campion (25) and thrift (35).

Cliff-ledge plants can grow in very small amounts of soil. They are often short, spreading plants like sea pearlwort (32) and sea milkwort (30). They may have fleshy water-storing leaves like golden samphire (19).

Scurvy grass (31), sea storksbill (28), red valerian (20) and wild carrot (21) are common higher up the cliff.

◀ Lichens

The slow-growing, dead-looking bodies of lichens do not seem very plant-like. They are really two plants – an alga and a fungus – living together in the same body. You will see bands of different lichens growing at different heights above the sea.

1 Leafy lichen (nearest to the sea)	3 Orange crusty lichen
2 Crusty lichen	4 Orange shrubby lichen (furthest from the sea)

Cliff birds

Many seabirds and some inland birds use sheltered cracks and caves in rocks near the sea for roosting and nesting. During the summer breeding season enormous numbers of seabirds will colonize a particular cliff or rocky island.

Some birds nest in burrows in the cliff soil. They may dig their own or use old rabbit warrens.

* Not to scale. Average body length given.

▲**Cormorant** 91cm
A sleek bird often seen perched on a rock or post with its wings outstretched to dry. It swims low in the water and dives for fish. Notice its hooked beak. Cormorants nest in groups on rocky ledges.

▲**Guillemot** 42cm
Guillemots look like razorbills but have slender pointed beaks and thinner necks. They live in enormous, noisy colonies on open cliff ledges. When flying, their wings make a whirring sound.

▲ **Puffin** 30cm
The colourful, grooved, parrot-like beak is smaller in winter as the outer layer is shed. Puffins swim and dive very well. They nest in rabbit holes or dig burrows in turf on cliffs on grassy islands.

▲ **Razorbill** 40cm
Look for the flat axe-shaped beak with white lines. Large colonies perch and nest on rocky ledges, often with puffins and guillemots. Like penguins they walk upright and are excellent swimmers.

◄ **Rock dove** 33cm
This is the ancestor of the domestic pigeon seen in towns, and makes the same 'oo-roo-coo' noise. It lives on rocky sea cliffs, where it nests in rocky crevices and caves, and eats seeds.

▲ **Manx shearwater** 36cm
During the breeding season this bird can often be seen gliding low over the waves or swimming in large flocks. As it flies, its wings show alternately black and white. It nests in burrows on cliffs.

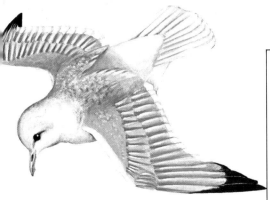

▲ Kittiwake 40cm
A gull which lives on the open sea except in the breeding season. It nests on steep cliffs or in caves. It swims and dives for fish and crustaceans. It gets its name from its call 'kitti-wa-ak'.

Young herring gulls

When gulls hatch, they look completely different from their parents. They are mottled brown, with brown beaks. After a year they are fully grown, but still have brown feathers and beaks. It takes another year for the adult feathers to grow. It is very difficult to tell the young of one gull from another.

Young gull

Adult herring gull

Chicks

▲ Herring gull 56cm
The most common coastal gull, with paler upper parts than the lesser black-backed gull. It eats worms, which it digs up, and breaks open molluscs by dropping them from a height on to stones.

▲ Great black-backed gull 68cm
This large, strong-winged gull steals from other birds. It robs nests, eating the eggs and young, and may kill other birds for food. Notice the pink legs and the massive yellow beak with a red spot.

▲ Lesser black-backed gull 53cm
Smaller birds than great black-backed gulls, with paler backs and wings. They live in colonies, usually on cliffs. As well as eating crabs and molluscs they take eggs from nests and eat rotting fish.

▲ Storm petrel 15cm
The smallest European seabird, once called 'Mother Carey's chicken' by sailors. If they saw one they expected storms. As it skims over the waves it looks as if it is treading on the water with its webbed feet.

▶ Gannet 91cm
This is a large bird which lives on the open sea. It catches fish by plunging into the sea with its wings folded back from as much as 30m. It breeds in a few enormous colonies on cliffs in the North Atlantic.

Coastal plants

Many plants only grow near the sea. They prefer the salty air and soil. Some of them are varieties of inland plants.

Many coastal plants have fleshy leaves, which contain stores of fresh water. These emergency stores can be used when rainwater is in short supply.

* Not to scale. The average height is given.

▲ **Sea lavender** 15-30cm
A common plant on salt-marshes and mudflats. It is not related to garden lavender, though its flowers are the same colour. It flowers in summer and autumn, often forming a purple carpet.

▲ **Wall pepper** 8cm
The tiny, fleshy, green leaves have a bitter, peppery taste, which gives the plant its name. It is common on shingle beaches and sand dunes. Look for the trailing stems and golden yellow flowers.

▲**Sea plantain** 15cm
Commonly found on cliffs and salt-marshes. Most of the leaves are long and fleshy and may be up to 30cm long. Other leaves are short and thin, like blades of grass. Spiky flowers appear in summer.

▲ **Danish scurvy grass** 20cm
This common plant is not a grass. It grows on damp sea cliffs and muddy seashore banks. Long ago sailors used to eat its heart-shaped leaves, which are rich in Vitamin C. This helped to cure a disease called scurvy.

▲ **Sea purslane** 40-60cm
A salt-marsh plant, which is also found on mudflats and sandy shores. Look for the thick, fleshy, spoon-shaped leaves and the tiny yellow-green flowers. The stems and leaves have a mealy white coating.

▲ **Golden samphire** 40-60cm
Found on salt-marshes, seawalls and among rocks on cliffs. The golden yellow flowers appear in late summer. The upright stem bears many small, thick, fleshy leaves, some with three points at the tip.

▲ **Sea campion** 15-20cm
Lives on firm shingle beaches, sandy shores and cliff ledges. It can grow in very little soil. On shingle, the plants cling to the surface, forming a mat. In summer it has white flowers, which are unmistakable.

▲ **Sea spurge** 20-30cm
A common plant on sandy shores. The greenish-grey, leathery leaves can store fresh water. It has yellowish-green flowers in summer and autumn. If broken, the stem and leaves produce a poisonous juice.

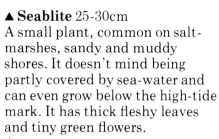

▲ **Seablite** 25-30cm
A small plant, common on salt-marshes, sandy and muddy shores. It doesn't mind being partly covered by sea-water and can even grow below the high-tide mark. It has thick fleshy leaves and tiny green flowers.

▲ **Hare's foot trefoil** 10-20cm
A common plant on shingle beaches and sand dunes. Look for the soft, easily recognised flowerheads, which look like hare's or rabbit's feet, and for the narrow clover-like leaves.

▲ **Viper's bugloss** 30-70cm
A very hairy plant which grows in dry gravelly places by the sea, and on limestone and chalk cliffs. The pink, trumpet-shaped flowers change to reddish-purple and then to brilliant blue.

▲ **Sea storksbill** 5-15cm
A small, soft, hairy plant, which grows close to the ground. It has long pointed fruits, which look like the beaks of storks. It is common on sand dunes and dry wasteground near the sea.

▲ **Common orache** Up to 100cm
This large plant is common in waste places by the sea. Look for the thin red lines on the stem and the tiny green flowers, which have no petals. The plant can be boiled, like cabbage, and eaten.

▲ **Slender thistle** 15-75cm
A very prickly plant which grows on cliffs and waste ground near the sea. In summer it has clusters of tiny purple flowers at the end of each stem. There are spiny 'wings' running up the stems.

▲ **Thrift** or **Sea pink** 10-15cm
This common seaside plant is easy to recognize, and is often grown in gardens. The stiff, grass-like leaves grow together forming a thick cushion. In summer it has clusters of pale pink flowers, each cluster on a long stem.

Edible seaside plants
Several wild seaside plants have been cultivated to produce important food plants.

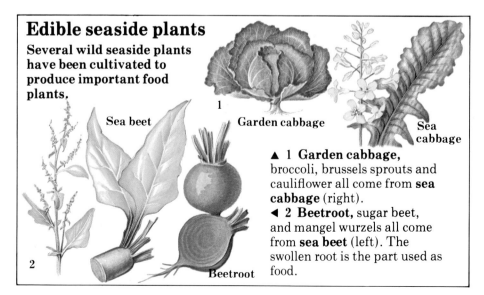

Sea beet

1 Garden cabbage

Sea cabbage

Beetroot

▲ 1 **Garden cabbage,** broccoli, brussels sprouts and cauliflower all come from **sea cabbage** (right).
◄ 2 **Beetroot,** sugar beet, and mangel wurzels all come from **sea beet** (left). The swollen root is the part used as food.

A salt-marsh

A salt-marsh is really a sheltered, low-lying area of land, soaked in seawater. The muddy soil is so salty that only certain plants and animals can survive the harsh conditions. Plants grow in bands or zones. Each zone is at a different height above sea-level. Salt-marshes are rich in birdlife. The birds search through muddy seawater creeks and pools for food.

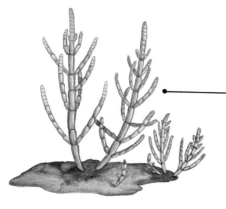

▲ Glasswort

Glasswort is a strange looking flowering plant. It has no leaves, and the tiny, green flowers have no petals. The fleshy, tubular stems can absorb and store fresh water. The roots are constantly in salt water but they can take in water without any salt.

Plants and levels

The fleshy spikes of glasswort (9) and the green bootlaces of eel grass (32) grow in the mud and are often covered by the tide. Mud is trapped between their stems and raises the level of the ground. Rice grass also traps mud with its roots.

Sea aster (8), sea purslane (17) and seablite (14) grow higher up, but are sometimes covered by the tide.

Well above high-tide level the spreading roots of sea meadow-grass (13) bind the muddy soil and make it firm. Whole areas may be carpeted with sea lavender (6). Cushions of thrift (5), shrubby sea purslane (17), and sea arrow-grass (1) are also common.

Painted lady butterfly

◄ Sea aster

Like most salt-marsh plants, the sea aster has fleshy water-storing leaves. It usually grows in large clumps, and its clusters of flowers brighten up the muddy creeks in late summer.

The painted lady butterfly has flown from North Africa to spend the summer in Europe.

▶ Rove beetles

At low tide, tiny rove beetles feed on algae and bits of rotting plants. They live in tunnels, which they dig at the top of muddy salt-marsh banks. Bubbles of air trapped in the tunnels help the beetles to survive if the tide rises too high.

Burrow entrance

Birds

Enormous numbers of waders, like Temminck's stint (26), dunlin (18) and godwits (11) poke about in the mud for small crustaceans and worms. At low tide, shelduck (24) hunt for snails, and eider duck (22) search for molluscs and crabs. The teal (23) feeds on glasswort.

Huge flocks of birds visit salt-marshes to feed, before flying on to winter homes or summer nesting sites.

▼ Flounders

Young flounders are found in muddy estuaries. When young they look like ordinary fish. As they get older, the left eye moves over to the right side of their flat bodies.

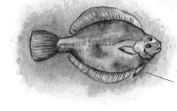

Young flounder

Adult flounder, living in a sandy estuary

Adult flounder, living in a muddy estuary

▲ The upper side of a flounder varies in colour to match the place where it lives. It feeds on cockles, crabs, shrimps and tiny fish, such as gobies.

Key

1 Sea arrow-grass	13 Sea meadow-grass	25 Oyster
2 Curlew	14 Seablite	26 Temminck's stint
3 Herring gull	15 Teal	27 Shrimp
4 Sea rush	16 Cord grass	28 Cockle
5 Thrift	17 Sea purslane	29 Barnacles
6 Sea lavender	18 Dunlin	30 Gribble
7 Heron	19 Sanderling	31 Lugworm
8 Sea aster	20 Knot	32 Eel grass
9 Glasswort	21 Cormorant	33 Ragworm
10 Redshank	22 Eider duck	34 Flounder
11 Godwit	23 Teal	35 Peppery furrow shell
12 Rove beetles	24 Shelduck	36 Shore crab

Leaf or needle?

Different kinds of tree

Two main types of forest grow in Europe. **Broad-leaved** forests grow in western and central Europe, while **coniferous** forests are usually found further north. Most broad-leaved trees are **deciduous** which means they lose their leaves in autumn and grow new ones the next spring. Coniferous forests are made up of **evergreen** trees which keep their leaves all the year round. They shed old needles and grow new ones continuously.

Water flows constantly up the tree from the roots and is lost through the leaves. In winter the roots cannot draw enough water from the cold soil. Broad-leaved trees drop their leaves to save water. Coniferous trees have waterproof leaves, and can therefore live further north and in mountains.

The shape of trees

Broad-leaved trees have a few large branches or limbs which sprout from the trunk and grow upwards to form the crown. Conifers have tall and slim trunks with many side branches. Their thin, flexible branches can bend under the weight of snow then spring up again without snapping.

Conifers grow very close to each other; a coniferous forest is quite dark inside.

Timber

Broad-leaved trees are also called **hardwoods** because their timber is very strong. Most hardwoods, such as oak or beech, grow very slowly and are not cut for timber until they are about a hundred years old. Conifers are called **softwoods**; they grow much faster and can be cut after only fifty years.

▲ The leaves of broad-leaved trees are arranged so that they catch as much sunlight as possible. The green pigment uses light and water to make food for the tree.

▲ Like most broad-leaved trees, conifers depend on the wind to carry male pollen to the female parts. When the female cone is ripe it splits and the seeds fall out.

▲ If the trunk of a conifer such as a pine is damaged, sticky resin oozes from the wound. This gums up insect pests that might otherwise bore holes in the wood.

Our varied woodlands

Woods and plantations

Long ago Europe was covered by dense forest. There are now very few ancient forests left. Most of the woodlands of today are greatly changed from their natural state; many have been planted. In **plantations**, the trees are the same age because they were planted at the same time.

Natural woodlands contain a mixture of tree species (kinds of tree), but usually one is more common than the rest. This is the **dominant species**. It grows better than the rest because it thrives on the type of soil found there. Oak trees do well on heavy, fertile, clay soils. Beech grows best on light, chalky soils and ash is often dominant on limestone hillsides. Conifers are found growing on thin, poor soils. Dense birch woods grow well on heaths and waste ground.

The canopy

Oak and ashwoods usually form an open canopy. The gaps between the trees and their leaves let light through, so many plants can grow in the shrub and ground layers. Beech forms a very dense canopy; this makes the ground below very shady with few plants growing. In conifer plantations it may be so dark that the only ground plants are fungi which do not need light to grow.

Using woodlands

Foresters cut woodlands in a number of ways. A tree may be **coppiced** by cutting it at ground level. It does not die and in time several new shoots grow from the stump. These can be cut later for poles. Deer were fenced out of coppiced woodland because they ate the bark and young shoots. In Royal hunting forests where deer roamed free the trees were cut 2–3 metres above the ground out of their reach. This is called **pollarding**.

▲ Some of the finest beechwoods grow on the steep slopes of chalk hills where they are called beech hangers.

▲ Modern conifer plantations have machines to cut down the trees, carry the timber and dig trenches for the new crop of trees.

▲ Hazel coppice was cut about every 7 years to provide poles which were split and woven into hurdle fences for sheep pens.

▲ Pollarded trees, such as these hornbeams, grow a cluster of branches where the trunk was cut. Pollarded willows are most familiar.

Looking up in broad-leaved woodland

Trees forming the woodland canopy and the bushy undergrowth of shrubs and saplings are rich in wildlife. An ability to climb or fly helps animals to explore habitats above the ground.

The grey squirrel (15) is an athletic climber. Long, sharp claws on its toes enable it to keep a grip, even on the smooth bark of beech trees. When alarmed it races up into the tree tops, jumping between branches with great skill.

Many woodland birds nest in tree holes. This protects them from predators such as jays (19) which are ruthless nest-robbers. Jays watch parent birds closely to find where they are nesting then steal the eggs and chicks.

Some birds search for food on tree trunks. Cracks and crevices in the bark harbour thousands of insects.

▲ The **female leaf-rolling weevil** (30) cuts and rolls hazel leaves into an egg container.

Key					
		11	Hawthorn	23	Tree creeper
		12	Ivy	24	Tawny owl
1	Oak	13	Honeysuckle	25	Redstart
2	Beech	14	Bracket fungus	26	Wren
3	Hornbeam	15	Grey squirrel	27	Bees
4	Ash	16	Wild boar	28	Purple emperor
5	Small-leaved elm	17	Fallow deer		butterfly
6	Sycamore	18	Wood pigeon	29	Purple hairstreak
7	Wild cherry	19	Jay		butterfly
8	Sweet chestnut	20	Pied flycatcher	30	Leaf-rolling weevil
9	Hazel	21	Nuthatch	31	Lichen moth
10	Maple	22	Green woodpecker	32	Hawfinch

leg hairs

▲ **Wild bees** (27) collect pollen from flowers and feed it to the larvae in the hive. The bee rolls the pollen into lumps which stick to hairs on the hind legs.

▼ The fore-wings of **lichen moths** (31) have the same colour and pattern as lichen. During the day they rest on lichen-covered tree trunks, safe from predators.

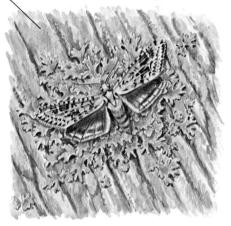

The nuthatch (21) is unusual; it crawls head first down the tree, where other birds climb upwards. Beside insects it also eats beech nuts and acorns; it wedges them into a crack before hammering them open with its bill.

The pied flycatcher (20) flies from its perch in the trees, chasing flying insects. The redstart (25), like the pied flycatcher, is a migrant from Africa and also lives chiefly on insects snapped up on the wing. The males display their bright red tail feathers to attract females.

Brightly coloured wings of butterflies also serve to attract mates. The purple emperor (28) and purple hairstreak (29) both live high in the tree tops.

◄ The **hawfinch** (32) has a massive beak with which it can crack open cherry stones, one of its favourite foods, in autumn and winter.

Trees of broad-leaved woodland

Broad-leaved woodland trees can be identified by their form, the shape of their leaves, and appearance of the bark. Some produce small green flowers which are wind pollinated and others have colourful blossom to attract insects. The great variety of seeds, nuts and berries provides food for many woodland animals.

*Not to scale

▲ **Hornbeam** Deciduous
A hornbeam has very hard wood. The leaves and bark may be mistaken for beech but the seeds are each joined to a thin leafy sail which carries them on the wind. The male and female catkins appear in March.

▲ **Sweet Chestnut** Deciduous
The flowers appear in July, later than on most trees, and are pollinated by insects. The glossy brown nuts fall from their spiny cases during October. They are very good to eat. Chestnut is often coppiced for fence posts.

▲ **Beech** Deciduous
The beech has smooth grey bark and grows over 40 metres high. The nuts are called beech-mast, are shed in October, and provide food for many animals. The leaves are very pale in spring, and turn bright gold in autumn.

▲ **Oak** Deciduous
The mighty oak can live for over a thousand years. It has deep roots and thick rough bark. The green flowers open in April or May and the acorns fall in autumn. Many birds and mammals eat acorns.

From acorn to oak tree

The mature oak tree may weigh more than 30 tonnes yet it starts life as an acorn weighing a few grams. Germination takes place in the spring. The acorn case cracks open and roots push down into the soil. The shoot grows up towards the light and soon the first pair of leaves unfurl.

leaves

shoot

root

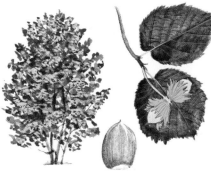

▲ Hazel Deciduous
Hazel is a very common species in the shrub layer. It has smooth brown bark. The flowers are wind-pollinated. They appear in February, long before the leaves. Hazel nuts are eaten by many animals.

▲ Holly Evergreen
Holly has shiny, prickly leaves. The trunk is covered with smooth, grey bark but the twigs are green. It flowers in May. The bright red berries ripen in September but stay on the tree throughout winter.

▲ Sycamore Deciduous
Sycamore grows very fast and is abundant in many woods. Yellowish flowers appear in April. They are rich in nectar and very attractive to bees. Squirrels are fond of nibbling the bark because the sap is sweet.

▲ Field maple Deciduous
A small tree, growing to about 10 metres. The leaves are the same shape as sycamore's but smaller. Many insects suck the sweet sap from the leaves. The flowers open in May with the leaves.

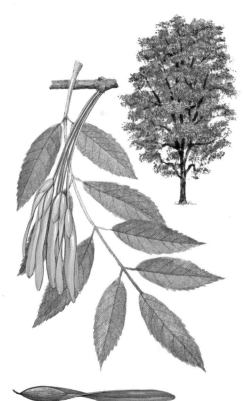

▲ Wild cherry Deciduous
Cherry has smooth, purple-brown bark. The large, white flowers blossom in April or May and are pollinated by bees. The cherries ripen during the summer and they are greedily eaten by birds.

▲ Hawthorn Deciduous
Hawthorn has sharp thorns on the twigs and branches. The white flowers, called May blossom, are sweet-scented to attract insects which pollinate them. The red berries are a favourite food of birds.

▲ Ash Deciduous
Ash has pale grey bark. In April the flowers appear in large green clusters before the leaves open. After pollination by wind, bunches of ash seeds or 'keys' are formed. Ash grows best in moist, fertile soils.

On the ground in broad-leaved woodland

Colourful wild flowers carpet the woodland floor wherever enough sunlight shines through the trees' leafy canopy. Many animals live or hide under fallen branches. The wood becomes riddled with holes made by the numerous insect larvae feeding on the dead wood. Old tree stumps are good places to look for fungi and mosses.

Butterflies fly in the summer. The speckled wood (**29**) and ringlet butterflies (**31**) settle on grasses after mating and lay their eggs. The white admiral (**30**) visits bramble flowers to feed on nectar.

The pygmy shrew (**19**) is Europe's smallest mammal. Nearby is a common shrew (**18**); they both hunt on the ground in a ceaseless search for food. They eat tiny animals living amongst leaf litter or in the soil, such as millipedes (**32**), centipedes (**34**), earthworms (**35**) and woodlice (**33**). Earthworms are very plentiful in woodland soil and the mole (**17**) digs underground tunnels to catch them.

The truffle (**38**) is a curious fungus that grows underground. It has a strong aroma which attracts mammals such as badgers, squirrels, hedgehogs and mice. They dig up and eat the fungus and spread its spores in their droppings.

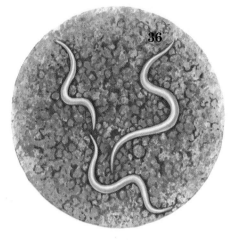

◀ **Nematodes** are tiny thread-like worms a few millimetres long. A teaspoonful of soil contains hundreds of them. They feed on dead plant and animal remains in the soil.

▶ **Worms** surface at night to take in leaves and other food, and to mate. Holding tight to its hole with the bristles on its body, the front end sweeps from side to side until it finds something good to eat. The worm cast is digested soil.

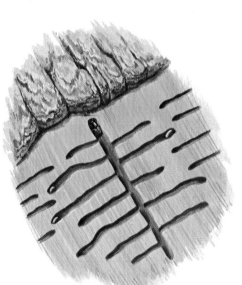

▲ **Oak bark beetles** chew a corridor under the bark along which their eggs are laid. On hatching, the larvae eat into the wood and form a network of spreading passages, often called galleries.

▼ Most plants try to spread their seeds as far as possible so they do not crowd each other. **Woodruff** seeds are covered in tiny hooked bristles which catch on the fur of mammals as they brush past, giving them a free ride to a new home.

barbed
seed head

worm cast

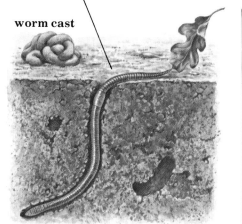

Key

1	Bramble	15	Broad-leaved helleborine	28	Snail	
2	Bluebell	16	Male fern	29	Speckled wood butterfly	
3	Ramsons	17	Mole	30	White admiral butterfly	
4	Early purple orchid	18	Common shrew	31	Ringlet butterfly	
5	Dog's mercury	19	Pygmy shrew	32	Millipede	
6	Ground ivy	20	Wood mouse	33	Woodlouse	
7	Wood anemone	21	Bank vole	34	Centipede	
8	Lords and ladies	22	Weasel	35	Earthworm	
9	Common dog violet	23	Hedgehog	36	Nematode	
10	Woodruff	24	Toad	37	Oystercap	
11	Herb robert	25	Woodcock	38	Truffle	
12	Red campion	26	Willow warbler	39	Chanterelle	
13	Yellow archangel	27	Song thrush	40	Stinkhorn	
14	Lily of the valley			41	Amethyst agaric	

Wild flowers

Wild flowers are the most colourful feature of the woodland ground layer. Bright petals and scents attract insects which pollinate the flowers. In some woods a few species, such as dog's mercury, bluebell and bramble are dominant.

*Not to scale.

▲ **Ramsons** or **Wood garlic**
Flowers April–June
Ramsons grows from a bulb and forms large patches in moist woods. Related to the onion family, the leaves smell strongly of garlic. The white flowers grow in clusters.

▲ **Common violet** Flowers April–June
Violets have heart-shaped leaves and rarely grow taller than 10 cm. The lower petals are marked with fine dark lines which guide insects to the nectar in the centre of the flower. The flowers have a pleasant, sweet smell.

▲ **Bluebell** Flowers April–June
Bluebells grow from a white, juicy bulb and they are very common in woods. The hanging clusters of bell-shaped flowers are sometimes pink or white. The stem grows about 30 cm tall, and when broken oozes a sticky juice.

▲ **Bramble** Flowers June–September
Brambles have very long, spreading stems. Sharp thorns on the stems and hooked prickles under the leaves protect them from deer. Many mammals and birds eat the blackberries in autumn.

▲ **Primrose** Flowers Feb–May
The primrose is a common early spring flower in woods and shady places. It has a rosette of soft, wrinkled leaves. The pale yellow flowers are borne on slender, pinkish stalks, growing about 10 cm tall.

▲ **Wood anemone** Flowers March–April
The wood anemone flowers before tree foliage shades the woodland floor. The delicate white flowers are tinged with pink. The stems are slightly hairy and grow about 20 cm high.

The art of pollination

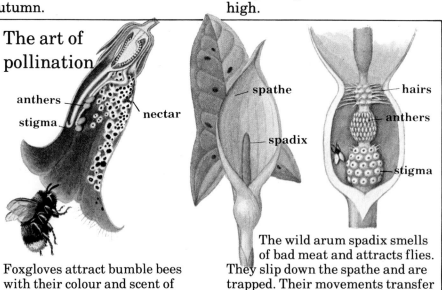

anthers
stigma
nectar
spathe
spadix
hairs
anthers
stigma

Foxgloves attract bumble bees with their colour and scent of nectar. As a bee crawls up the flower tube, pollen sticks to it, pollinating the next foxglove.

The wild arum spadix smells of bad meat and attracts flies. They slip down the spathe and are trapped. Their movements transfer pollen to the stigmas. Next day the hairs shrivel and they can fly away.

Broad-leaved helleborine
Flowers July–September
This plant grows to about one metre high. It does well in beech woods but also appears in conifer plantations. The flowers are pollinated mainly by wasps. ▼

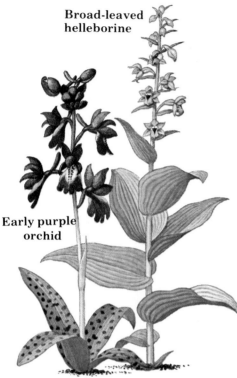

Broad-leaved helleborine

Early purple orchid

Dog's mercury Flowers March–April
Dog's mercury is particularly common in woods growing on rich soil. The greenish-yellow flowers are borne on stalks about 3 cm long. The leaves are poisonous. ▼

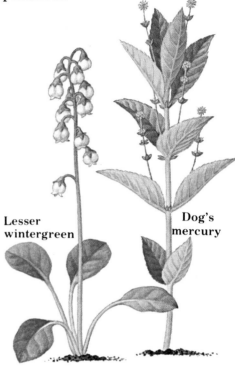

Lesser wintergreen

Dog's mercury

▲ **Wood sorrel** Flowers April–May
Wood sorrel is a small, delicate plant that grows in shady woods. The leaves fold tightly shut at night and they have a sour taste like rhubarb. The pale white petals are marked with pink streaks.

▲ **Early purple orchid** Flowers April–May
Early purple orchids are especially common in coppiced woodland. The leaves are marked with dark blotches and the flowers vary in colour from faint pink to deep purple.

▲ **Bilberry** Flowers April–June
Bilberry can form thick carpets on the floor of coniferous woods, especially if the soil is sandy. It has woody stems and small leaves. The berries are edible.

▲ **Lesser wintergreen** Flowers June–August
Lesser wintergreen is found in shady pine forests. Clusters of round, pink flowers hang from a stalk growing to about 20 cm tall.

▲ **Herb paris** Flowers May–July
Herb paris is an unusual plant which grows on fertile, chalky soils. Each plant has just four broad leaves and produces only one green flower. The fruit is a black berry. Herb paris belongs to the Lily family.

▲ **Herb robert** Flowers April–October
Herb robert is a common woodland plant and flowers throughout the summer. The stems are usually red and slightly hairy. It often grows in dense clumps to a height of 30 cm.

▲ **Ground ivy** Flowers March–June
Ground ivy is a low, creeping plant whose flowers are among the first to appear in spring. It has a square stem from which sprout pairs of dark green, wrinkled leaves that have a strong, bitter smell.

91

Mammals

Mammals are warm-blooded vertebrates. Their fur coats keep them warm, especially in winter. After mating, the babies develop inside their mother until they are born. They suckle her milk until they are old enough to feed themselves.

*Not to scale. Average adult body length given.

▲ **Wild boar** 150cm tail 25cm
Wild boars are armed with dangerous tusks. They rummage through the woods for acorns, roots and bulbs. The sow gives birth to up to 12 young in April or May. Boars are increasingly common in parts of Europe.

▲ **Badger** 75cm tail 18cm
Badgers leave their setts at dusk. They are very clean animals and dig their toilet pits away from the sett. Eating almost anything, they use their long claws to dig for worms, roots and bulbs. Up to 4 cubs are born in March..

▲ **Grey squirrel** 26cm tail 21cm
The grey squirrel was introduced from America last century and is now very common. It eats buds, bark, leaves and shoots and stores nuts in winter. Up to 4 young are born in spring in a leafy nest or drey. It does not have ear tufts.

▲ **Red squirrel** 25cm tail 21cm
The red squirrel is a native European animal. It is found in pine woods and the seeds of fir-cones are one of its favourite foods. It will also eat nuts, berries, mushrooms and birds' eggs. It is no longer as common as the grey squirrel.

▲ **Pine marten** 45cm tail 25cm
The pine marten has a slim body, sharp claws and a long bushy tail which help it clamber easily through the tree branches. It hunts squirrels, birds and small mammals. Large numbers have been trapped for their fur and they are now quite rare.

▲ **Wood mouse** 9cm tail 9cm
Wood mice breed several times in summer. The young mice grow quickly and leave the nest when they are only 2 weeks old. They eat plants and store nuts and seeds for winter. They are common throughout Europe.

▲ **Bank vole** 10cm tail 4.5cm
The bank vole builds a nest of grass and moss on the ground or under a log. There are up to 6 young in each litter. They feed mostly on grass seeds and berries but will also eat snails and insects.

▲ **Common shrew** 7cm tail 5cm
The common shrew is active by day and night all the year round. It has a long whiskered snout for sniffing out worms and insects. It feeds mostly under ground. The common shrew has a very shrill squeak.

▲ **Red deer** 200cm tail 15cm
Red deer live in herds and feed on grasses, mosses, shoots and buds. The stags shed their antlers in winter and grow a new set during spring. Red deer mate in September but the young are not born until spring.

▲ **Roe deer** 130cm tail 4cm
Roe deer are common in Europe. They live in small family groups and feed on grasses, shoots and leaves. They run with great bounding strides when alarmed, and are good swimmers. They feed at dawn and dusk.

▲ **Fallow deer** 135cm tail 18cm
Many centuries ago fallow deer were introduced into royal hunting forests to provide sport. They eat leaves, bark, nuts and berries. Two fawns are born in May or June. In winter the white spots on its coat disappear.

▲ **Weasel** 30cm tail 8cm
The weasel is bloodthirsty and fearless. It will attack animals much larger than itself, such as rabbits. Mice, voles and young birds are also eaten. Up to 6 young are born in spring and the mother defends them bravely.

▲ **Hedgehog** 28cm tail 3cm
The hedgehog rolls into a ball when frightened but it can run quite quickly despite having short legs. It eats worms, insects and small mammals. It sleeps during the day and hibernates in winter.

▲ **Fox** 80cm tail 40cm
The fox is a cunning hunter, creeping quietly towards its prey before pouncing. It eats mostly small mammals and birds and sometimes insects, especially beetles. It often lives in the same burrow as a badger.

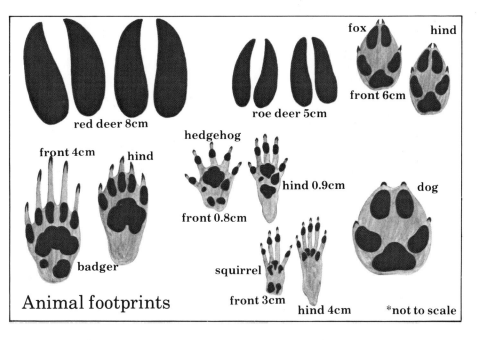

red deer 8cm

roe deer 5cm

fox

hind

front 6cm

front 4cm

hind

badger

hedgehog

hind 0.9cm

front 0.8cm

dog

squirrel

front 3cm

hind 4cm

*not to scale

Animal footprints

▲ **Mole** 15cm tail 3cm
The mole has short, dark, velvety fur. With its large forepaws it digs tunnels in search of worms and insects. It is almost blind and finds food by smell. Molehills show where a mole has pushed soil from its tunnel.

Birds

Birds are warm-blooded and covered with feathers which make up their *plumage*. In many species the male or cock bird has a more colourful plumage than the female or hen. The young are fed by their parents until ready to leave the nest. The great variety of bird calls and songs are a striking feature of woodland.

*Not to scale. Average adult body length given.

▲ **Chaffinch** 15 cm
The chaffinch is very common in Britain. A cup-shaped nest is built in a fork of a tree or bush in April or May. They feed the young with insects in summer but eat mainly seeds at other times.

▲**Great tit** 14 cm
The great tit is easily recognized by the black band which runs from its chin to its tail. It nests in tree holes and will use nest boxes. It eats insects, nuts and seeds. The song sounds like 'tea-cher tea-cher'.

▲ **Jay** 34 cm
The jay is a shy but handsome bird with its pinkish plumage and bright blue wing patches. It eats eggs, young birds, insects, snails and seeds. In autumn it stores hundreds of acorns for the winter.

▲ **Sparrowhawk** Male 28 cm
Female 38 cm
The sparrowhawk is a predator and hunts small birds in woodlands and over farmland. 4–6 eggs are laid in May on a nest of sticks built up a tree, usually next to the trunk.

▲ **Tawny owl** 38 cm
The tawny owl has soft wing feathers specially suited for silent flying at night. It hunts small mammals, birds and insects, especially beetles. 3–4 round, white eggs are laid in a hollow tree in April.

▲ **Willow warbler** 11 cm
Willow warblers are summer migrants arriving from Africa in April. They fly back in September. Most of their time is spent in the shrub layer where they search for insects. Up to 8 eggs are laid in May.

▲ **Green woodpecker** 32 cm
The green woodpecker has a loud laughing call as it flies from tree to tree. It eats insects on the bark and is also fond of ants which it captures on the ground with its long tongue. It digs a hole in a tree to lay its eggs.

▲ **Great spotted woodpecker** 23 cm
The great spotted woodpecker is a very handsome bird with a strong bill. It chips away the tree bark to get at insects and their larvae. 4–7 whitish eggs are laid in a hole in a tree during May.

▲ Coal tit 11 cm
The coal tit has a white patch on the back of its head. Common in coniferous woodland, it feeds largely on insects. The nest is usually built in a tree-hole where 6–10 eggs are laid during April–May.

▲ Long-eared owl 36 cm
The long-eared owl inhabits coniferous woodland. The tufts on its head are not its ears. It feeds at night on mice, voles, birds and insects. It lays 4–5 white eggs in an old nest of a pigeon or hawk.

▲ Siskin 11 cm
The siskin is found mostly in coniferous woodland. It is a bird of the tree tops and eats tree seeds and a few insects. The nest is built in a tree and 4–5 eggs are laid in April–June. The male (in front) is the more colourful.

▲ Nuthatch 14 cm
The nuthatch lives and feeds in the tree layer. It crawls along branches in search of insects but it will also eat seeds and berries. It wedges hazel nuts into the bark before chipping them open. Nuthatches nest in tree-holes.

▲ Tree creeper 13 cm
The tree creeper is also called the tree-mouse after the way it scuttles up tree trunks looking for insects. The nest is usually built behind a piece of loose, peeling bark. 5–9 eggs are laid in May or June.

▲ Pheasant Male 84 cm Female 59 cm
The pheasant is a game bird and was introduced from Asia about 200 years ago. They feed on shoots, seeds and insects. About 12 eggs are laid on the ground in April–June.

woodpecker

wood pigeon

song thrush

woodcock

The variety of nests

Woodpeckers dig out a hole in a tree trunk and lay their eggs on a bed of wood chips. Woodcocks' eggs are laid on the ground where they blend against a background of dead leaves.

Song thrushes build a cup-shaped nest of dead grasses and leaves and lined with mud. It is wedged in a forked branch. Wood pigeons construct a very flimsy platform of twigs in a tree or bush.

▲ Woodcock 34 cm
The woodcock is a native game bird. It nests and feeds on the ground. The long bill is pushed into soft soil or mud to capture worms. When disturbed it flies away very quickly and low, dodging between the trees.

Looking up in coniferous woodland

Coniferous woodlands are darker, and usually quieter, than broad-leaved woodlands. Conifers grow very close to each other, whether in a natural forest or a plantation. There is therefore little light under the tree layer to allow many shrubs or ground plants to grow.

Rhododendron (8) bushes grow well in deep shade and they are often planted under conifers to give cover for game birds such as pheasants. Their pink flowers attract bees which collect the pollen and drink the nectar.

Two red deer stags (11) are fighting over females which are called hinds. They butt each other with their antlers in a trial of strength. Eventually the weaker stag tires and is chased away.

The goshawk (12) is a dashing hunter. It flies very quickly, dodging between the trees, to surprise and catch birds. Back at the nest it tears its prey into pieces, small enough for the chicks to swallow.

A goldcrest (19) is also feeding its young. The delicate cup-shaped nest is slung under a conifer branch and is built with moss, spiders' webs and feathers.

Coal tits (17) often lay their eggs in an old woodpecker's nest, but first they line the hole with feathers. They are very brave birds and sit tight on the eggs and hiss angrily should an enemy, such as a pine marten, try to rob the nest.

◀ A **squirrel** has used its sharp teeth to gnaw away the outside of this **pine cone**. It turns the cone in its fore-paws and nibbles the seeds in just the same way as we eat corn on the cob.

▶ **Pine sawfly larvae** feed on pine needles. They look like caterpillars but the adults are closely related to wasps.

A pine marten (**10**) is stalking a red squirrel (**9**). For the squirrel there is no escape in the trees because the pine marten is also a good climber and, like the squirrel, it has a bushy tail which helps it to balance. The pine marten also hunts birds in the trees and will eat their eggs and chicks.

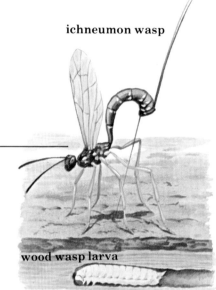

ichneumon wasp

wood wasp larva

▲ The **ichneumon wasp** uses its long egg-laying tube to bore a tiny hole into tree bark and deposite an egg on a larval wood wasp. When the egg hatches the ichneumon larva feeds on the wood wasp larva.

▼ The **crossbill** uses its curious twisted beak for opening pine cones to get at the seeds inside.

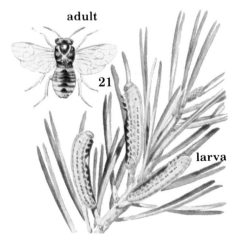

adult

21

larva

Key		11	Red deer
		12	Goshawk
1	Silver fir	13	Eagle owl
2	Larch	14	Great spotted woodpecker
3	Spruce		
4	Scots pine	15	Crossbill (male)
5	Birch	16	Crossbill (female)
6	Aspen	17	Coal tit
7	Rowan	18	Siskin
8	Rhododendron	19	Goldcrest
9	Red squirrel	20	Ichneumon wasp
10	Pine marten	21	Pine web sawfly

Trees of coniferous woodland

Coniferous woodland is dominated by evergreen trees which keep their leaves throughout the year. Many are important timber trees and are grown in plantations. The size and shape of the cone and the arrangement of the leaves are useful clues for their identification.

*Not to scale.

▲ **Rowan** or **Mountain ash** Deciduous
Rowan has smooth, grey bark and seldom grows higher than 15 metres. Clusters of creamy white flowers open in May. By August the shiny red berries are ripe.

▲ **Rhododendron** Evergreen
A shrub which forms dense thickets, it is often planted to shelter breeding game birds. It grows best on poor, sandy soils. The pink or purple flowers, with brown spots, open in May-June.

▲ **Silver fir** Evergreen
Grows naturally in mountain ranges in central Europe but has also been widely planted. It grows up to 70 metres high. The needles are 1–2.5 cm long, thin and flat with two white stripes underneath.

▲ **Aspen** Deciduous
This tough tree can survive in cold mountain regions. The leaves flutter and tremble in the wind, showing grey underneath. Male and female catkins are borne on separate trees. The woolly seeds float away in June.

▲ **Scots pine** Evergreen
Huge forests of Scots Pine grow in northern Europe. The blue-green needles are 3–7 cm long and grow in pairs. Male cones shed pollen in May. The female cones take two years to ripen. The branches are rusty-red.

▲ Douglas fir Evergreen
This timber tree was brought
over from America 150 years
ago. It grows very quickly – to 30
metres in 30 years. The needles
are 2–3 cm long. Douglas firs are
known to live for over 750 years.

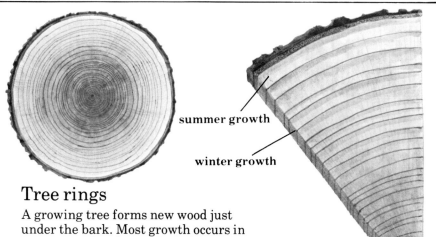

Tree rings

A growing tree forms new wood just
under the bark. Most growth occurs in
summer and makes wide, light bands.
Narrow, dark bands show winter growth.
You can tell a tree's age by counting the
number of dark rings. Start in the centre
and work outwards.

summer growth

winter growth

▲ Silver birch Deciduous
The trunk is covered with
smooth, peeling white bark
around dark, knobbly patches.
The seeds have a delicate pair of
wings and are blown from the
female catkins in October. Birch
trees only live for about 80 years.

▲ Larch Deciduous
Larch is very common in
plantations. Bright green
needles (2–3 cm long) sprout in
March. The pinkish, young
female cones appear in April. A
larch tree can grow as much as
10 cm a week in summer.

▲ Norway spruce Evergreen
This tall, graceful tree is widely
planted in northern Europe for
timber and Christmas trees. The
pale brown female cones grow up
to 18 cm long. It has shallow
roots and is easily blown over in
gale force winds.

On the ground in coniferous woodland

Coniferous woods are usually very shady and the soil is often poor. The plants found on the woodland floor can thrive under these conditions. Bilberry (3) and cowberry (4) can only grow on poor soils. Creeping ladies' tresses (8), lesser wintergreen (10) and buckler fern (14) grow well in deep shade. A great variety of mushrooms and toadstools appear during autumn even in the darkest woods.

Wood ants (21) cover their underground nests with a huge mound of dead pine needles. This helps to keep the colony warm in winter during which they eat their stores of seeds. In summer they feed on insects, especially caterpillars. Worker ants travel high into the trees to collect them. If the nest is threatened they squirt stinging acid from tail glands at their attackers.

A black woodpecker (19) feeds on wood ants. It also hacks open rotting logs in search of insects. A capercaillie (18) struts through his territory uttering a loud rattling call that warns off rival males. The female lays 5–8 eggs at the base of a pine tree. Capercaillies eat the buds and shoots of young conifers as well as berries and seeds.

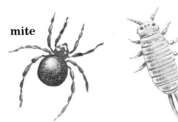

mite

springtails

◀ More than 200,000 **springtails** and **mites** can be found in one square metre of coniferous forest floor. They feed on the dead needles.

▶ The **puffball fungus** ripens into a dry bag which contains millions of tiny spores. Clouds of spores escape through an opening at the top and are carried away by the wind.

▲ The **two-banded longhorn beetle** (13-22 cm) is common in pine woods. Its larvae live and feed in rotting wood for 2 or 3 years before emerging as adults.

▼ The seeds of **cow-wheat** (12) are mistaken by **ants** for their pupae because they look so similar. Ants help to spread the seeds by carrying them back to their nest.

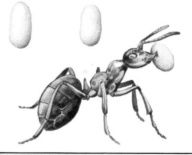

spores

At night the wild cat (**16**) prowls in search of small mammals and birds. By day it rests in a rocky lair. Here, in summer, the female gives birth to 4 or 5 kittens. She fiercely defends her young and spits angrily at intruders. Wild cats are encouraged in coniferous plantations because they keep down the numbers of rodents and rabbits which eat young tree shoots.

Key

1	Bracken	22	Boletus
2	Bramble	23	Fly agaric
3	Bilberry	24	Puffball
4	Cowberry	25	Wood mushroom
5	Foxglove	26	False chanterelle
6	Heather		
7	Moss (*Hycolomium* *splendeus*)		
8	Creeping ladies' tresses		
9	Ball moss		
10	Lesser wintergreen		
11	Wavy hair grass		
12	Cow-wheat		
13	Polypody fern		
14	Buckler fern		
15	Polecat		
16	Wild cat		
17	Bank vole		
18	Capercaillie		
19	Black woodpecker		
20	Scotch argus butterfly		
21	Wood ants		

Insects and other tiny animals

Animals without backbones are called invertebrates. They cannot grow as big as birds or mammals because they have no skeleton to support them. There are thousands of different species of invertebrates in our woodlands. They feed on a great variety of foods and are themselves eaten by other animals.

*Not to scale. Average adult body length given. Ws = wingspan.

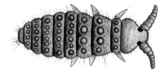

▲ **Springtail** 2mm
The springtail can jump by flicking the fork-shaped tail which is curled under its body. They are abundant in the soil and feed on dead leaves. They die in autumn and their eggs lie dormant through the winter.

▲ **Speckled wood butterfly**
14mm Wingspan 36mm
The speckled wood is very common. It can often be seen fluttering along woodland paths and in sunny clearings. It breeds throughout the summer. The green caterpillars eat grasses.

▲ **Wood white butterfly** 15mm
Ws 35mm
The wood white is found on sunny days flying around paths and clearings. On dull days it clings to the underside of a leaf. The caterpillars eat plants of the pea family, such as vetch.

▲ **Purple hairstreak butterfly**
14mm Ws 35mm
The purple hairstreak flies high among the tree tops in July and August. It likes to feed on sweet chestnut flowers. The eggs are laid on oak leaves which the caterpillars eat.

▲ **Silver-washed fritillary butterfly** 22mm Ws 60mm
The silver-washed fritillary is found in woods where there are plenty of violets for its caterpillars to eat. The eggs are usually laid on an oak trunk.

▲ **Oak eggar moth** 20mm Ws
50mm
The oak eggar is a brown furry-bodied moth which flies in July and early August. The males fly by day as well as by night when the females are active. The caterpillars feed on bramble and hawthorn leaves.

▲ **Oak tortrix moth** 7mm Ws
18mm
The oak tortrix is a small nocturnal moth which is very common in oak woods. It flies in June and July. The eggs hatch in May and the caterpillars feed on oak leaves. It is also called the Green oak beauty.

▲ **Magpie moth** 18mm Ws
43mm
The magpie moth is very common and easy to recognize. It flies in July and August. The caterpillars feed on hawthorn, raspberry and gooseberry bushes and they are often found in gardens as well as woods.

The life cycle of the Purple Emperor

▶ The eggs hatch in July.

The caterpillars start feeding on leaves.

They hibernate in autumn in a silk cocoon. In spring they begin feeding and growing.

▶ In June they pupate – a hard case forms round them as they hang upside down from a stalk.

▲ After 2 weeks the case cracks open and the adult butterfly crawls out.

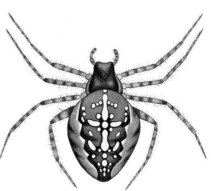

▲ **Garden spider** Male 11mm Female 20mm
The garden spider builds a web to catch flying insects. It has poison fangs and bites its victim to death. In autumn the female dies after laying eggs which hatch next spring.

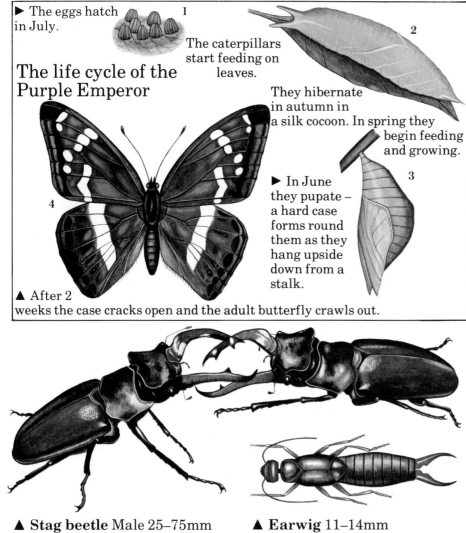

▲ **Stag beetle** Male 25–75mm Female 22–45mm
Stag beetles feed on sap oozing from wounds in oak bark. The males have upper jaws like antlers, and fight over females in summer. The eggs are laid on rotting wood where the larvae live.

▲ **Earwig** 11–14mm
Earwigs are found under bark, stones and fallen leaves. They feed on leaves, flowers and fungi spores. Their pincers are used for defence. In autumn up to 60 eggs are laid under a stone and guarded by the female.

▲ **Hedge snail** Shell width 17mm
Hedge snails are very common in and around woodlands where they feed on ground-level plant leaves. The shell colour can vary a great deal. In winter they hibernate in a hole in the soil.

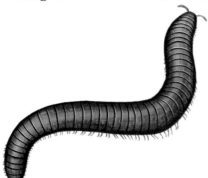

▲ **Millipede** 15–50mm
Millipedes live under logs and stones and they feed on dead plant remains. When alarmed they coil up as though they were dead. They can also squirt a stinking yellow liquid at their enemies.

▲ **Centipede** 20–30mm
The centipede is found amongst dead leaves and under logs and stones. It is a predator and feeds on spiders, woodlice and worms. It catches food with its front pair of legs which are poisonous pincers.

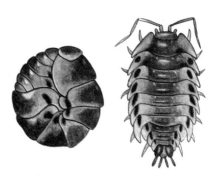

▲ **Woodlouse** 15mm
Woodlice live in the damper parts of woods and feed on dead plant remains. They hide under stones and behind bark and roll into a tight ball if disturbed. Woodlice are closely related to crabs and shrimps.

Plants without flowers

Woodlands contain a great variety of plants that never produce flowers or seed. They grow from tiny spores which are much smaller than the seeds of flowering plants. Large number of mushrooms and toadstools appear in autumn. Fungi like these digest dead leaves and rotting wood.

Do not eat or taste any wild fruit or fungi unless you are quite sure they are harmless. Fungi marked ! are very poisonous: do not touch.

▲ Many lichens can be found on tree trunks or rocks but the **pixie cup** grows on the soil. Spores are formed around the rim of the cup.

▲ **Mosses** grow from spores released from tiny capsules which dry open in the wind and shake out their contents.

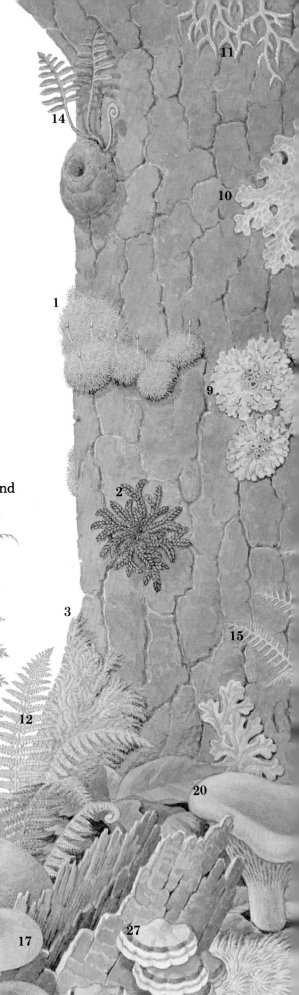

▼ The *Pellia* liverwort grows on damp soil and wet rocks. The spore capsule grows from a curly green leaf called a thallus.

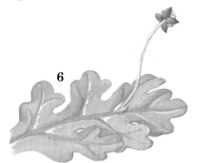

6

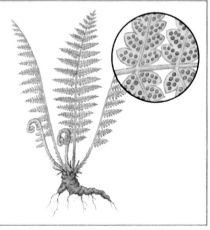

▲ The **male fern** sprouts from a large woody root. Under the fronds are clusters of spores.

▲ Flies eat the smelly slime of the **stinkhorn fungus** and spread its spores in their droppings.

▲ 'Umbrella' fungi have **gills**. Millions of minute spores fall from gaps between the gills.

▲ **Bird's nest fungi** spores form eggs which lie in the cup until raindrops wash them out.

16

Key		
1 Moss (*Dicranoweisia cirrata*)	7 Moss (*Brachythecium rutabulum*)	16 Hart's tongue fern
2 Liverwort (*Frullania dilatata*)	8 Orange lichen	17 Sulphur tuft fungus
3 Moss (*Hypnum cupressiforme*)	9 Lichen (*Parmelia caperata*)	18 Stinkhorn
4 Pixie cup lichen	10 Lungwort	19 Bird's nest fungus
5 Moss (*Dicranum scoparium*)	11 Lichen (*Ramalina farinacea*)	20 Chanterelle
6 Liverwort (*Pellia epiphylla*)	12 Male fern	21 Death cap (POISON)
	13 Buckler fern	22 Fly agaric (POISON)
	14 Polypody fern	23 Boletus
	15 Hard fern	24 Sickener (POISON)
		25 Wood blewit
		26 Saffron milk cap
		27 Bracket fungus (*Trametes versicolor*)

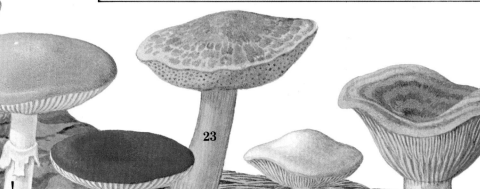

22
21
23
24
25
26

The web of life

Food sources

All the living things in a wood depend on others for their food. Each, in turn, is food for other species.

The primary source of food is in plants. In a wood there are plant foods in the form of leaves, wood and fruits. Another source of food is the dead and decomposing remains of plants and animals.

Leaves

Leaves provide a great deal of the food – one oak tree may have over 100,000 leaves – so there are vast numbers of leaf-eating animals. Aphids, for example, suck leaf juices, and breed quickly in the summer when leaves are plentiful. Over 5,000 million aphids can live in one hectare of woodland. They can grow wings and fly away to search for new supplies if the leaves become too crowded. Aphids are eaten by lacewings, which in turn are eaten by spiders.

Caterpillars are tremendous leaf-eaters and are eaten by many birds. Migrants, such as warblers, fly all the way from Africa to raise their young in summer on the abundant supply of juicy caterpillars.

Other sources

Wood is a food for beetle larvae, which chew tunnels behind the bark. Even here they are not safe from woodpeckers.

Dead leaves and animals are an important source of food for 'decomposers'. Worms, for example, eat dead leaves and help make the soil fertile. In turn they provide food for birds and mammals.

The large quantities of seeds and fruits produced each year provide a feast for voles, wood mice, and birds such as chaffinches.

Food chains

As we have seen, warblers eat spiders which eat lacewings which eat aphids which feed on leaf juice. This list can be made into a food chain:

leaves-aphid-lacewing-spider-bird

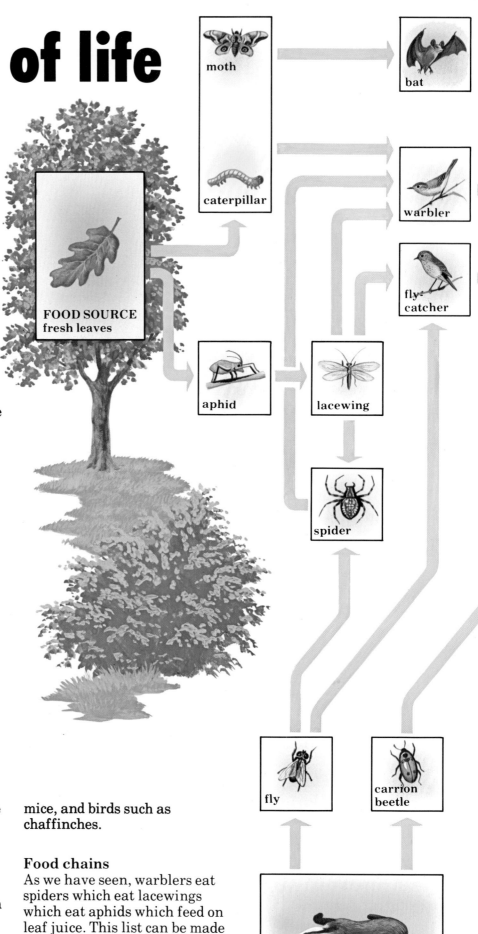

FOOD SOURCE
fresh leaves

moth

bat

caterpillar

warbler

fly-catcher

aphid

lacewing

spider

fly

carrion beetle

FOOD SOURCE
carrion

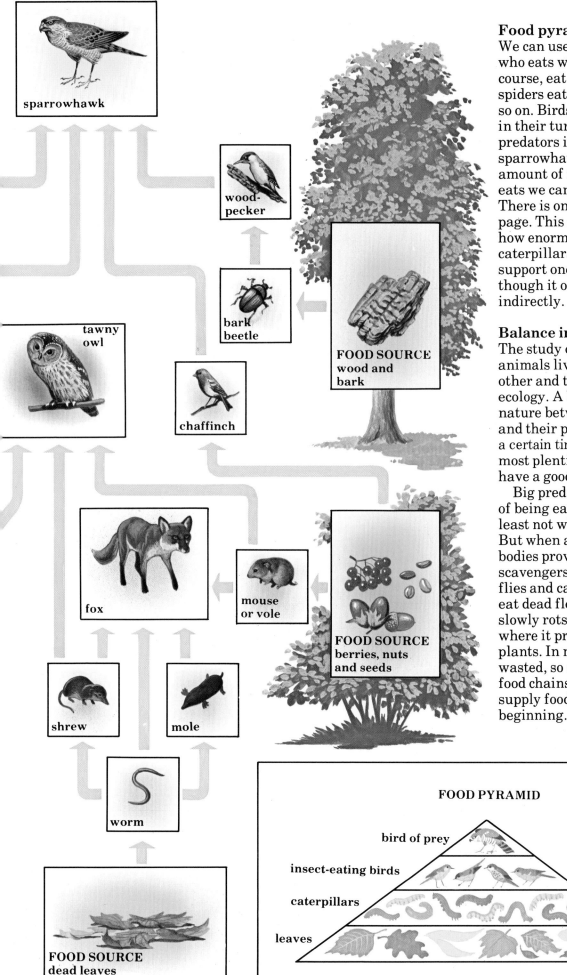

sparrowhawk

wood-pecker

bark beetle

FOOD SOURCE
wood and bark

tawny owl

chaffinch

fox

mouse or vole

FOOD SOURCE
berries, nuts and seeds

shrew

mole

worm

FOOD SOURCE
dead leaves

Food pyramids

We can use food chains to show who eats what. Warblers, of course, eat many spiders, and spiders eat many lacewings, and so on. Birds, such as warblers, in their turn may be eaten by predators including sparrowhawks. To show the amount of food each predator eats we can draw a food pyramid. There is one at the bottom of the page. This shows, for example, how enormous numbers of caterpillars are needed to support one sparrowhawk, though it only feeds on them indirectly.

Balance in nature

The study of how plants and animals live in relation to each other and their habitat is called ecology. A balance exists in nature between the predators and their prey. Animals breed at a certain time when food is most plentiful and the young will have a good chance of survival.

Big predators are in no danger of being eaten themselves – at least not while they are alive. But when animals die their bodies provide food for scavengers, such as the larvae of flies and carrion beetles, which eat dead flesh. What remains slowly rots back into the soil where it provides nutrients for plants. In nature nothing is wasted, so animals at the end of food chains will eventually supply food for plants at the beginning.

FOOD PYRAMID

bird of prey

insect-eating birds

caterpillars

leaves

A meadow

A meadow is a field in which a farmer grows a mixture of grasses. The grass crop may be cut and dried to make hay, or turned into silage. A meadow used for grazing cattle and sheep is called a pasture.

Permanent meadows and pastures make an almost natural habitat. Yellow ragwort (17) is poisonous to cattle, but is the main food plant of the caterpillars (6) of the colourful cinnabar moth (5).

New shoots of creeping thistle spring up everywhere from its network of underground stems. The feathery fruits of spear thistles (10) are the favourite food of goldfinches (9). In summer, meadows may be yellow with buttercups, dandelions and yellow rattle (20). Kingcups (34), sedges (26) and horsetails (36) are common in damp meadows.

Many different invertebrates live in a meadow. The drab colour of the meadow grasshopper (25) makes it difficult to spot. Its familiar chirrup is made by it rubbing its back legs against its wings.

The lapwing (3), a common meadow bird, doesn't make a proper nest. It lays its mottled olive eggs in a grass-lined scrape in the ground.

▼ Grasses
Amongst the cultivated grasses in meadows you will also find wild grasses. Grasses are difficult to identify. Look carefully at the arrangement of the flower-heads. This will help you to tell them apart.

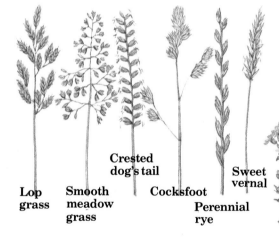

Lop grass **Smooth meadow grass** **Crested dog's tail** **Cocksfoot** **Perennial rye** **Sweet vernal**

▼ Mole cricket (rare)
The mole cricket has large, sharp-edged front legs for digging its long burrow. Crickets 'sing' to attract a mate by rubbing their front wings together. The horn-shaped mouth of the burrow makes the sound much louder.

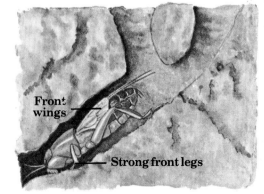

Front wings

Strong front legs

Key

1	Swallow	14	Dyer's greenweed	29	Meadow vetchling
2	Skylark	15	Yorkshire fog	30	Mole
3	Lapwing	16	Pale clouded yellow	31	Sexton beetles
4	Rabbit	17	Ragwort	32	Vole
5	Cinnabar moth	18	Meadowsweet	33	Cuckoo flower
6	Cinnabar moth caterpillars	19	Tufted hair grass	34	Kingcup
7	Meadow brown	20	Yellow rattle	35	Slippery snail
8	Timothy grass	21	Ox-eye daisy	36	Horsetail
9	Goldfinch	22	Italian rye	37	Bugle
10	Spear thistle	23	Sorrel	38	Lesser celandine
11	Black knapweed	24	Hammock spider	39	Bird's-foot trefoil
12	Orange tip	25	Grasshopper	40	Lesser yellow trefoil
13	Partridge	26	Sedges	41	Great plantain
		27	Green-winged orchid	42	Crab spider
		28	Small copper	43	Seven-spot ladybird

▼ Oil beetle

The eggs are laid on the ground. The louse-like larvae (1) crawl up the stem of a plant, such as a dandelion. They wait on the flowers (2) to cling to a bee (3). In the hive the beetle larvae feed on nectar and pollen (4). They go through several stages before developing into adult beetles.

Adult female laying eggs

▼ Dor beetle

These beetles help to break down dung and mix it with the soil. Dor beetles often carry mites, so they are also called 'lousy watchmen'. The larvae feed on dung in tunnels, dug by the females, under cowpats.

Cow-pat

Adult dor beetle, with mites on its abdomen

Larva in tunnel filled with dung

Larger animals

The larger wild animals of farmland are harder to observe. Many of them feed at night or in the early morning. During the day they shelter in hedgerows, amongst crops or around buildings. (NB. Some of the most common farmland mammals, reptiles and amphibians are described in other books in this series.)

* **Not to scale. Average body length (excluding tail) given unless otherwise stated. Ws = wingspan.**

▲ **Feral cat** 50-65cm
This is a domestic cat which has gone wild. Such cats no longer depend on people for food or shelter. They are common around farms, where they hunt small mammals, and may attack poultry.

▲ **Polecat** 33-38cm
This fierce, bad-smelling mammal is related to the weasel. It hunts at night for rats, mice, rabbits, lizards and birds. The male is called a Hob and the female a Jill. Found mainly in Wales.

▲ **Slow-worm** 45cm
This snake-like reptile is a legless lizard. It lives under logs and stones in quiet damp places. It feeds on slugs, snails and worms. Always handle a slow-worm carefully, as its tail easily breaks off.

▲ **Dormouse** 7·5cm (tail 6·5cm)
This plump, nocturnal mammal lives in hedgerows, feeding on nuts, fruit and berries. Many die of cold during their long winter hibernation. They are less common than they were, due to the loss of their woodland habitat.

▲ **Dartmoor pony** 12·2 hands tall (1 hand = 10cm)
A pony is a small horse, less than 14½ hands tall. Wild ponies still roam parts of the mountains and moorlands of Britain, as they have done for centuries. They live almost wild. You may see ponies like this grazing alongside sheep.

▲ **Pipistrelle bat** 4cm Ws 20cm **Long-eared bat** 5cm Ws 25·5cm
Bats are mammals. Their wings are skin, stretched over their long finger-bones. They are active at dusk and dawn, so they hunt by using 'echo location'. As they fly, they send out high-pitched squeaks. These are reflected from objects, like nearby insects, so that the bat hears where they are.

▲ **Yellow-necked mouse** 10cm
This mouse, with its vivid yellow chest patch, lives in southern Britain. Like the smaller, but more common wood mouse, it lives in woods, hedges and fields. It feeds on berries, seeds, nuts, snails and insects.

▲ **Field vole** 10cm
Notice the blunt snout and short ears. This very common vole lives in coarse grass on roadside verges and pastures, and in hedgerows. If you look carefully, you may find vole tunnels and pathways amongst the grass roots.

▲ **Harvest mouse** 5-7cm
This is one of Britain's smallest mammals. It lives in hedgerows, cornfields and other grassy places. As it moves from one grass stalk to another it coils its tail around the stalk for extra support.

▲ **Brown rat** 24cm (tail 18cm)
These rodents are very common on farmland. They spend the winter in buildings, in sewers and on rubbish tips. In summer they move out into the fields and hedgerows in search of food. Keep away from rats: they may carry diseases.

▲ **Brown hare** 54cm
Hares are larger than rabbits, with longer ears and legs. They spend the day amongst cover, coming out at dusk to feed on grass, cereals and vegetable crops. Found on farms and open downland. Young hares are called leverets.

▲ **Rabbit** 40cm
A rabbit warren is a system of underground tunnels where a colony of rabbits lives. Rabbits feed at dawn and dusk on any fresh green food. They can cause a lot of damage to crops, pastures and young trees.

▲ **House mouse** 7-9cm
This rodent eats grain and food scraps. It marks its territory with urine, which gives off the familiar 'mousy' smell. The female may produce over 50 young a year. Common in walls, barns, hedgerows and haystacks.

Animal signs

The larger animals are rarely seen, but there are many clues to tell you which animals have passed by.

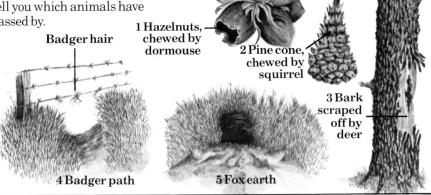

Badger hair

1 Hazelnuts, chewed by dormouse

2 Pine cone, chewed by squirrel

3 Bark scraped off by deer

4 Badger path

5 Fox earth

A hedgerow

Hedgerows are the living fences around fields. Natural forests and woodlands are rapidly disappearing, and many hedges are being destroyed. This is disastrous, for Britain's hedges and roadside verges are now the last great reservoirs of wildlife.

The commonest hedgerow tree is the hawthorn (5). Oak (1), hazel (3) and holly (6) can also put up with being cut back by the farmer. These plants form a thick barrier to keep farm animals in the fields.

Over 40 species of birds visit hedgerows to nest or feed. Chaffinches (4) and tree-sparrows (2) nest in the trees. Wrens (7) prefer the thick jungle of plants round the base of the trees.

In spring bluebells (12), and primroses (15) carpet sunny hedgebanks. In summer foxgloves (19), red campion (17) and willowherb (21) make a splash of colour amongst the grasses. Field-mice (8), shrews (25) and voles (36) make tiny runs and tunnels through the grass to carry food back to the safety of their nests. Like the rabbits, mice keep a careful look-out for the stoat (22), which is also looking for food.

The toad (26) comes out at night to feed on slugs (43) and other invertebrates. In autumn look for the feathery fruits of old man's beard (44).

▲ Verge plants
Only the toughest plants can survive on roadsides. They must put up with people and traffic, as well as with being mown. Many are low-growing plants, and flower and fruit quickly.

▶ Cuckoo pint
This plant is pollinated by small insects such as flies, carrying pollen from another cuckoo pint. They are attracted by the smell and trapped by the downward-pointing hairs (2), until the female parts of the flowers (1) have been fertilized. Later, the sheath (3) withers and poisonous red berries develop.

Sheath (3)

Spadix

Hairs (2)

Male flower

Female flowers (1)

Flies

Key

1	Oak	**15**	Primrose	**30**	Germander speedwell
2	Tree-sparrow	**16**	Garlic mustard	**31**	Herb Robert
3	Hazel	**17**	Red campion	**32**	Hawthorn shieldbug
4	Chaffinch	**18**	Common lizard	**33**	Mottled umber moth
5	Hawthorn	**19**	Foxglove	**34**	Spike rushes
6	Holly	**20**	Cow parsnip	**35**	Comfrey
7	Wren	**21**	Broad-leaved willowherb	**36**	Bank vole
8	Long-tailed field mouse	**22**	Stoat	**37**	Peacock butterfly
9	Bullfinch	**23**	Lesser celandine	**38**	Winter moth
10	Wall pennywort	**24**	Adder	**39**	Great crested newt
11	Wood spurge	**25**	Common shrew	**40**	Brown-lipped snail
12	Bluebells	**26**	Toad	**41**	Kingcup
13	Wood anemone	**27**	Horsetail	**42**	Silver-washed fritillary
14	Hedge sparrow	**28**	Lesser burdock	**43**	Black slug
		29	Gatekeeper	**44**	Old man's beard

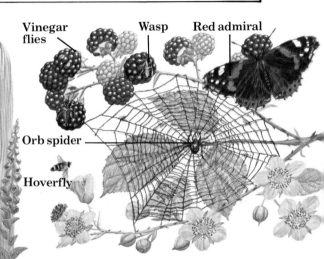

Vinegar flies · Wasp · Red admiral · Orb spider · Hoverfly

▲ Life in a bramble

Many insects visit bramble flowers or feed on the fruits. The orb spider lurks in the centre of its hammock-like web, waiting to trap insects. Hedgerow birds feed on blackberries, and eat flies, aphids and caterpillars.

▼ Dormice

The dormouse is active at dusk, searching for nuts, berries and fruit. Its summer nest is a hollow ball of grass, leaves and honeysuckle bark. Inside, the female may produce up to two litters a year, each with 3 to 5 young. The winter nest is usually below ground.

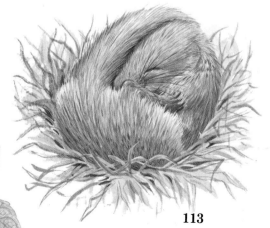

113

Birds

Farmland is rich in many kinds of food and attracts large numbers of birds. The changing patterns of farming are affecting birdlife. By removing hedges and trees to make larger fields, farmers are destroying valuable cover, food and nest sites. Birds that cannot adapt to these constant disturbances are now less common.

* Not to scale. Average body length given unless otherwise stated.

▲ **Wood-pigeon** 41cm
This is the largest European pigeon, and is one of the farmers' worst bird pests. Huge flocks descend on farm crops to eat seeds, grain and the leaves of vegetable plants such as cabbage. In winter they also eat clover.

▲ **Starling** 22cm
A beautiful and very common bird on all kinds of farmland, often in huge flocks. They help the farmers by eating wireworms. They can be a pest, because in winter they may eat large quantities of artificial cattle feed.

◄ **Kestrel** 35cm
A common sight on farmland, along motorway verges and even in towns. It hovers on fluttering wings, head still, searching for mice, voles and invertebrates below. Then it drops silently, like a stone, on its prey.

▲ **Barn owl** 34cm (top) **Little owl** 22cm (bottom)
Barn owls are no longer common on farmland. Their favourite nesting sites are old stone buildings, many of which are now being replaced by concrete buildings.
   The more successful little owl is often seen at dusk on farmland. Both owls feed mainly on insects and small mammals.

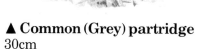

▲ **Common (Grey) partridge** 30cm
This game bird is becoming less common. It nests in the rough grass at the edge of fields. These areas are being cleared, together with the hedgerows, to make larger fields that are more efficient to farm.

▲ **House-martin** 13cm (top) **Swallow** 19cm (bottom)
These summer visitors are common around farm buildings, where they dip and soar as they catch insects on the wing. The house-martin makes its cup-shaped mud nests under the eaves of buildings. Swallows make saucer-shaped mud nests in the rafters of buildings, such as cowsheds.

▲ Stone curlew 40cm

These rare summer visitors prefer the southern parts of Britain. They live on open, bare ground such as chalk downs and ploughed fields. Here they feed at dusk on snails, insects and worms. Notice the large yellow eye.

Female Male

▲ Lapwing, peewit 30cm

Common everywhere on farmland, especially on pastures, where it nests on open ground. Look for the long crest, and the broad rounded wings seen in flight. Listen for its characteristic 'peese-weet' call.

▲ Skylark 18cm

Listen for the wonderful, endless, bubbling song of the skylark as it hovers high over grassland, pastures and cornfields in summer. It nests in crop fields and pastures, and feeds on insects and seeds.

▲ Pied wagtail 18cm

Look for the long tail, constantly bobbing up and down as this smart little black and white bird struts about, looking for insects. It is common around farms, especially in the winter.

Male Female

▲ Yellowhammer 16cm

This common bunting is found everywhere on farms, especially in hedgerows. Listen for the call 'A little bit of bread and no cheese'. It feeds mainly on seeds and grain, with some insects in summer.

▲ Greenfinch 14cm

This hedgerow bird has a powerful beak for eating wild fruits, berries and seeds. In winter it feeds on rosehips, weed seeds and dropped grain in farmyards. Notice the yellow wing-bars.

The crow family

Magpie

Jay

Jackdaw

Rook

Hooded crow

Carrion crow

These members of the crow family are common on farmland. Look for the untidy twig nests of rooks and jackdaws high up in tall trees. Rooks and crows eat a lot of grain, as well as inverte-brates, such as leatherjackets. Magpies are now as common in towns as in the country. The colourful jay, with its harsh call, is more often heard than seen, as it prefers woods to fields.

Tiny animals

These are invertebrates: animals without backbones. There is no shortage of food on farmland, so enormous numbers of invertebrates may be found in the soil, amongst the crops and in the hedgerows.

* Not to scale. Average body length given unless otherwise stated. Ws = wingspan.

▲ **Field cricket** 20-26mm
Lives in well-drained grassland, especially on sandy soils. During the day it stays in its burrow, which it digs beneath a stone. At night the male chirps loudly by rubbing its front wings together. More common in Europe.

▲ **Damsel bug** 8-9mm (left)
Green shield bug 12-13·5mm (right)
The hard, protective forewings of beetles meet edge to edge, but the forewings of the beetle-like bugs above are transparent at the tips and may cross.

The damsel bug sucks the body fluids of other invertebrates. The shield bug sucks plant juices. Both are common in the summer.

▲ **Ground beetle** 14-16mm
This is one of the commonest ground beetles. It lives in the soil in fields, meadows and hedgerows. During the day it hides under stones and plant remains. At night it feeds on plants and other small invertebrates.

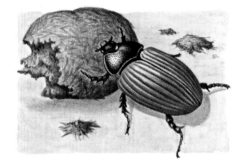

▲ **Dung beetle** 5-7mm
This is one of the commonest dung beetles. It lives and feeds on the dung of horses, cattle and sheep. A cow produces about seven tonnes of dung a year, so there is plenty of food for the developing larvae to eat!

▲ **Hoverfly** 8-11mm
You can spot this common type of hoverfly by its odd-looking snout. In early summer the female lays eggs on a plant overhanging a cowpat. The larvae fall into the dung where they feed and develop.

The life-cycle of the seven-spot ladybird

1. The eggs are laid in spring, usually near a colony of aphids. **2.** The fierce larvae feed on aphids for three weeks. They eat up to 500 aphids, and moult three times. **3.** Fully-grown larvae attach themselves to leaves. Their skins harden, and form a pupal case. Inside, the adult ladybird beetle develops.

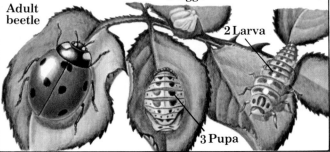

Adult beetle

1 Eggs

2 Larva

3 Pupa

▲ **Harvestman** male 4-7mm, female 5-8mm
Harvestmen belong to the same group as spiders, but have longer legs. They hunt for invertebrates and plant remains in grassland, wasteground and near buildings. Common in damp autumn conditions.

▲ Froghopper 5-6mm
This plant-sucking bug is common in grassland. The eggs hatch into nymphs. These produce the protective, frothy cuckoo-spit in which they live and feed. The adults hop when disturbed. Their colour varies greatly.

▲ Meadow brown Ws 44mm, caterpillar 25mm
The female has larger orange patches on its forewings than the male. The caterpillars feed on grasses at night, in autumn. During the day they hide amongst grass roots. It overwinters as a caterpillar.

▲ Wall butterfly Ws 44mm, caterpillar (larva) 30mm
These common butterflies are often seen sunning themselves. The caterpillars feed on grasses. There are two generations each year. The second one may overwinter as pupae.

▲ Five-spot burnet Ws 30mm caterpillar 25mm
The bright red spots on this day-flying moth warn birds that it is not good to eat. Common on dry grasslands, meadows and downs in the south. The caterpillars feed on clover and bird's-foot trefoil.

▲ Large white Ws 70mm, caterpillar 40mm
A familiar sight in fields, meadows and gardens. The caterpillars feed on the leaves of the cabbage family and can severely damage farm crops. There may be three generations a year. Overwinters as a pupa.

▲ Hairy snail shell width 7-9mm
Very common in meadows and waste places. In dry weather, the snail attaches itself to the underside of a leaf. The mouth of its shell becomes covered with a thin membrane to stop the snail drying up.

▲ Buff-tailed bumble bee 20-27mm
One of the commonest species of bumble bee. Look for the silvery-grey tip to its abdomen. The nest, made of moss and dry grass, is often built in a disused mouse-hole in a meadow or hedgebank.

▲ Woodlice *Porcellio scaber* up to 17mm (left) *Oniscus asellus* up to 16mm (right)
Woodlice are the land-living relatives of crabs and lobsters. They quickly dry up and die if removed from their damp habitat, under stones, bark and leaf litter. They feed at night on dead wood, plant roots and ripe fruit. These common woodlice cannot roll up.

▲ Netted slug 30-40mm
This small slug is found everywhere in fields and meadows. It can be a great nuisance to the farmer when it eats crops. The colour varies from browny-yellow to blue-black.

A cornfield

A cornfield is only a temporary home for wild plants and animals. For much of the year the growing corn provides food and shelter for animals. Wild plants compete with the corn for light, water and minerals. Farmers try to remove these unwelcome visitors, as they reduce the yield of the crop. At harvest time wild plants are removed along with the corn. The nests and burrows of animals are destroyed. Any plants and animals that remain will be burnt with the stubble or buried by the plough.

Like many cornfield plants, poppies (12) and fat hen (9) are annuals. They survive the harvest by producing many light seeds which are dispersed by wind and animals. Their seeds remain alive in the soil for many years. The underground stems and roots of couch grass (23) and bindweed (10) can survive being disturbed by the plough. Wild oat (5) is a great nuisance, as its seeds are harvested with the corn. Sainfoin (28), and rye grass may be sown with the corn. They grow through after the harvest to provide pasture for the following year.

Game birds like partridges (27) and pheasants (16) search through the stubble for food. At dusk a tawny owl (2) hunts for voles, and bats (6) catch insects.

◄ **Harvest mouse**
In summer, this tiny mouse builds a hollow nest of grass just above the ground. It is about 10 cm in diameter. Several litters of up to 9 young are produced. In winter harvest mice live in haystacks or in burrows below ground level.

▶ **Invertebrates**
Invertebrates which feed on grain can reproduce and spread quickly in cornfields. Wireworms and eelworms damage roots, corn thrips suck out plant sap, and leaf beetles eat the leaves. Sawfly larvae eat their way up the stem. If all these animals survive many plants are weakened and may die.

Field damsel bug

Leaf beetle

Leaf beetle larva

Corn thrip

Ground beetle

Wireworm

Eelworm

Wheat stem borer sawfly larva

Key

1 Skylark
2 Tawny owl
3 Four-spot dragonfly
4 Collared dove
5 Wild oat
6 Pipistrelle bat
7 Adder
8 Charlock
9 Fat hen
10 Field bindweed
11 Cornflower
12 Poppy
13 Sparrow
14 Common vetch
15 Corncrake
16 Pheasant
17 Hare
18 Rabbits
19 Corn bunting
20 Bramble
21 Toadflax
22 Bank vole
23 Couch grass
24 Grove snail
25 Earthworm
26 Centipede
27 Grey partridge
28 Sainfoin
29 Clover
30 Wood pigeon
31 Yellow-necked mouse
32 Quail
33 Long-tailed field mouse

▼ **Hamsters**

When pet hamsters escape they may survive, and breed in the wild. They live in burrows at the edges of fields. In towns they may live on allotments, where they can be a pest. They are active at night, feeding on grain, seeds and nuts.

Sticky mouse-ear

119

Plant pests

Any animal or plant which attacks crops, fruit trees or domestic animals is called a pest. Many crop pests are invertebrates. They breed quickly. It is usually the larvae which kill or weaken plants. Larger animals, such as pigeons, rabbits and deer, are also important crop pests.

* Not to scale. Average body length given.

▶ **Frit fly** 1·5mm
In spring, this fly lays its eggs on cereals. The larvae burrow into the main shoot. The leaves become yellow and the plant is weakened.

▶ **Wireworm** 20mm
This larva is one of the worst agricultural pests. It eats the roots and young shoots of many crops. It lives in the soil for several years before hatching into a click beetle.

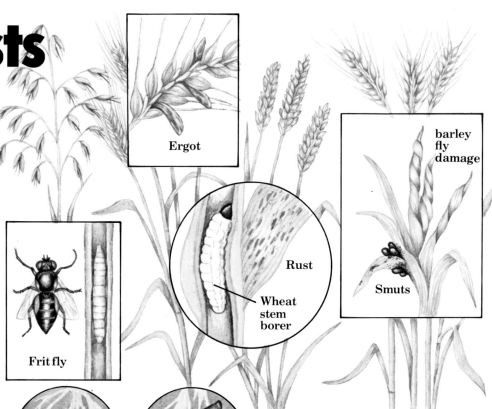

Ergot

barley fly damage

Rust

Wheat stem borer

Smuts

Frit fly

◀ **Leatherjacket** 20-40mm
This is the larva of a cranefly. Large numbers live in the soil, feeding on and damaging the underground parts of plants.

larva

adult

Turnip moth

Slug

Woodlouse

▲ **Flea beetle** 3mm
The larvae eat into turnip and radish leaves, making tunnels called 'mines'. The adults eat the leaves, making them wilt and die.

▶ **Eelworm** 1mm
These tiny roundworms damage roots. The male is worm-like, but the female swells to form a 'cyst', filled with eggs and young.

▲ **Carrot root fly** 6mm
The small flies lay their eggs at the base of young carrots in early summer. The larvae eat their way into the developing carrots.

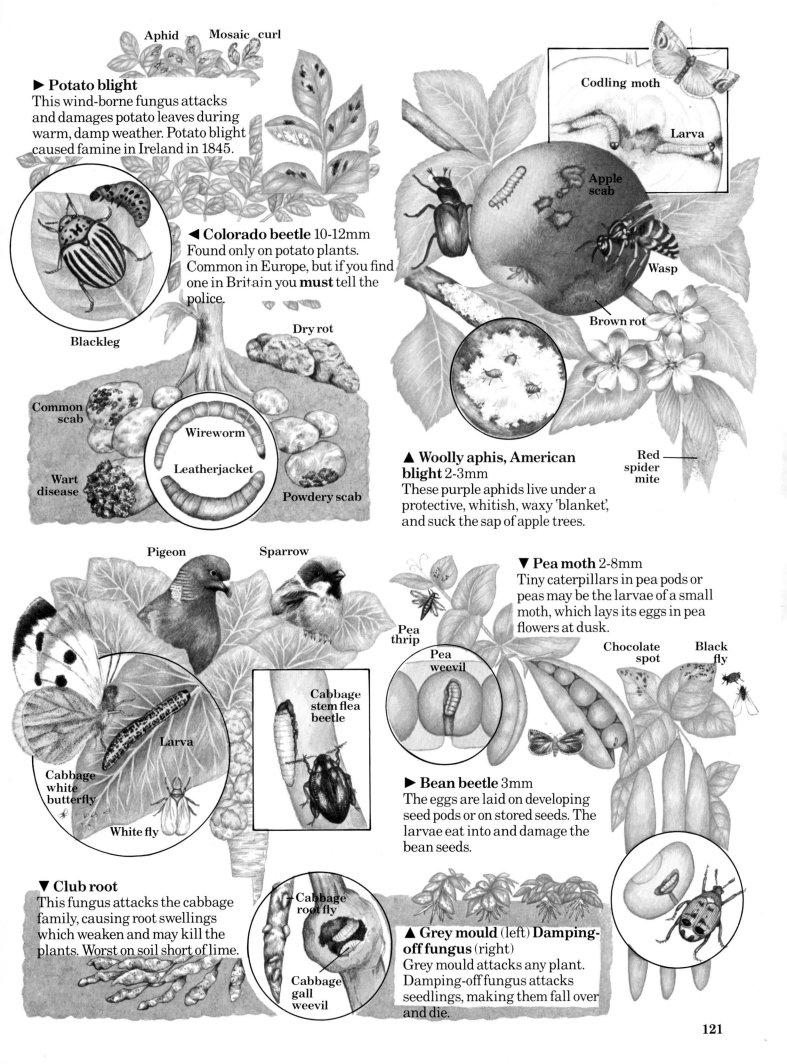

Aphid Mosaic curl

▶ Potato blight
This wind-borne fungus attacks and damages potato leaves during warm, damp weather. Potato blight caused famine in Ireland in 1845.

◀ Colorado beetle 10-12mm
Found only on potato plants. Common in Europe, but if you find one in Britain you **must** tell the police.

Blackleg

Dry rot

Common scab

Wireworm

Leatherjacket

Wart disease

Powdery scab

Codling moth

Larva

Apple scab

Wasp

Brown rot

Red spider mite

▲ Woolly aphis, American blight 2-3mm
These purple aphids live under a protective, whitish, waxy 'blanket', and suck the sap of apple trees.

Pigeon   Sparrow

Cabbage stem flea beetle

Larva

Cabbage white butterfly

White fly

▼ Club root
This fungus attacks the cabbage family, causing root swellings which weaken and may kill the plants. Worst on soil short of lime.

Cabbage root fly

Cabbage gall weevil

▼ Pea moth 2-8mm
Tiny caterpillars in pea pods or peas may be the larvae of a small moth, which lays its eggs in pea flowers at dusk.

Pea thrip

Pea weevil

Chocolate spot

Black fly

▶ Bean beetle 3mm
The eggs are laid on developing seed pods or on stored seeds. The larvae eat into and damage the bean seeds.

▲ Grey mould (left) **Damping-off fungus** (right)
Grey mould attacks any plant. Damping-off fungus attacks seedlings, making them fall over and die.

Animal pests

Plants and animals living on or inside other animals are usually called parasites. They rarely kill but may cause great suffering. Animals in poor condition because of parasites or disease are often unfit for sale. In Britain, strict laws control the movement, sale and slaughter of infected animals.

* Not to scale. Average body length given.

▶ Foot and mouth disease

This dreaded disease is caused by a virus, which spreads rapidly. It affects mainly cattle, pigs and sheep. In Britain infected animals **must** be slaughtered to stop the disease spreading.

▼ Coccidiosis

This disease is caused by *protozoans*. These single-celled animals multiply rapidly, causing a lot of damage to the intestines of birds. They form cysts in the lining of the intestine. These then burst, releasing more protozoans, causing severe bleeding. Infected birds are usually destroyed.

1 Young enter intestine lining and develop into adults
2 Infected cell containing adults
3 Healthy cells
4 Schizont bursts, causing bleeding

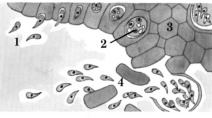

▶ Scaly leg mite up to 0·75mm

These yellowish crusts are caused by mites. These tiny parasites tunnel deep into the skin. Found in dirty hen-houses.

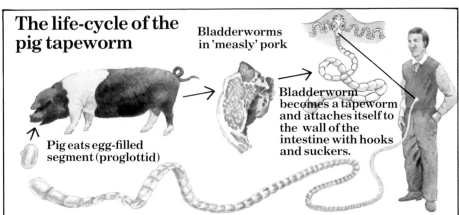

The life-cycle of the pig tapeworm

Bladderworms in 'measly' pork

Bladderworm becomes a tapeworm and attaches itself to the wall of the intestine with hooks and suckers.

Pig eats egg-filled segment (proglottid)

An adult tapeworm may be 7 metres long, and contain more than 1000 proglottids.

▶ Roundworms up to 30cm

Large numbers of these worms can live in the intestines of many animals, even humans. In pigs large roundworms may be as thick as a pencil.

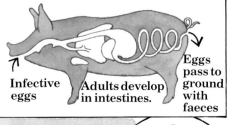

Infective eggs

Adults develop in intestines.

Eggs pass to ground with faeces

Ringworm

Lice

Blisters

▲ Mange

Caused by tiny mites which burrow and feed under the skin, which becomes rough, wrinkled and sore, and the animal scratches continually.

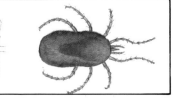

▲ Feather mite (left), Red fowl mite (right) up to 0·75mm

Feather mites feed on skin scales. Red fowl mites suck the blood of roosting poultry. They live in cracks in the perches.

◀ Lice up to 2mm

These common, biting insects live as *ectoparasites* on the skin and amongst the feathers of birds. They feed on skin flakes and bits of feather. They breed very fast.

Ringworm

Lungworms
in lungs

▲ Lungworm (Husk) up to 8cm
Eggs, laid in the lungs, hatch into
larvae which are coughed up and
swallowed. They pass out in the
dung. They develop on the grass,
and are picked up by other cows as
they graze.

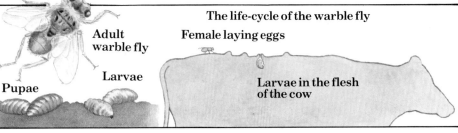

◄ Lice up to 2mm, **Mange mites**
up to 0·75mm
These biting lice and tunnelling
mites cause irritation and soreness
to cattle.

▼ Warble fly 13-14mm
The eggs are laid on hairs on the
legs or belly. For nine months the
larvae burrow through the flesh.
They travel to the animal's back.
When fully developed they fall to
the ground, pupate and hatch into
adult flies.

The life-cycle of the warble fly

Adult
warble fly

Female laying eggs

Larvae

Pupae

Larvae in the flesh
of the cow

► Liver fluke 3cm
These *endoparasites* belong to the
invertebrate group called
flatworms. The adults live in the
liver. They have a complex life-cycle
involving two hosts: the sheep, and
a small snail found on damp
pastures.

▼ Common sheep tick up to
4mm
This insect sucks blood, and
transmits diseases. Eggs are laid
on the grass. The newly-hatched
larvae cling to a passing sheep to
feed and grow.

▼ Greenbottle, Blow fly 7-11mm
These shiny flies lay eggs in moist,
dirty sheep's wool. The larvae feed
on the sheep's flesh, causing pain
and eventually death.

Greenbottle   Larvae in wool

The life-cycle of the liver fluke

swimming
larva on
grass

Eggs
pass out
in dung

Adults develop in
the sheep's liver

Larva

Larvae
develop
inside
snail

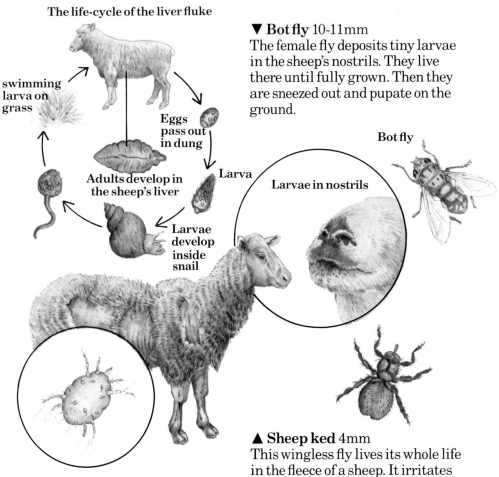

Larvae in nostrils

Bot fly

▼ Bot fly 10-11mm
The female fly deposits tiny larvae
in the sheep's nostrils. They live
there until fully grown. Then they
are sneezed out and pupate on the
ground.

▲ Scab
Tiny mites living on the skin of the
sheep cause scabs to form. These
are very itchy, and irritate the
sheep a great deal, causing it to rub
off patches of wool and skin.

▲ Sheep ked 4mm
This wingless fly lives its whole life
in the fleece of a sheep. It irritates
the skin.

* By law, all sheep must be 'dipped'
in disinfectant each year to kill
pests, particularly the mites which
cause sheep scab.

A farmyard

This is a difficult place for wild plants and animals to inhabit. There is little soil for plant-roots, and animals are disturbed by farmworkers, machinery and livestock.

Despite the bustle and noise swallows (1) and house-martins (2) weave and swoop through the farmyard, catching flying insects. Their mud nests are built in the cow-shed roof. A pied wagtail (9) catches insects, while sparrows (8) wait to share the chickens' (34) grain.

At dusk a barn owl (3) sets out on silent wings to hunt for mice (15). Later, a fox (4) searches the farmyard for food, such as rats (38), mice, hedgehogs (32) and poultry.

The special 'adventitious' roots of ivy (13) help to attach its stems to the wall as they climb upwards. Hart's tongue fern (22) and leafy liverwort (18) grow in damp, shady areas. An alga called Pleurococcus (19) forms green, powdery streaks on damp tree-trunks, walls and roofs.

In the undisturbed parts of the farmyard there are typical wasteground plants, like coltsfoot (33), willowherb (27), dead nettle (25) and pineapple weed (37). These give shelter to a toad (26), a lizard (21), and many invertebrates.

▼ Wall invertebrates
Many invertebrates hide in damp cracks in crumbling walls. This spider traps its prey by spinning silken tubes in the cracks between the bricks. Tiny mounds of fine soil may be the entrance to an ant's nest.

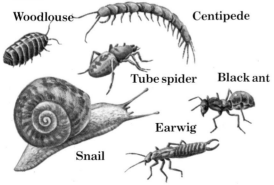

Woodlouse   Centipede

Tube spider   Black ant

Earwig

Snail

Dutch barn

Bulk grain silo

Combine harvester

HARVEST

▶ Dung flies
These furry yellow flies are a common sight in farmyards or on cowpats. After mating, the female lays eggs in a cowpat. The larvae tunnel through the dung, feeding on it, then pupate in the soil beneath. They play an important part in breaking down the dung and mixing it with the soil.

Key

1 Swallow
2 House martin
3 Barn owl
4 Fox
5 Store cattle (Friesians)
6 Rhode Island Red cockerels
7 Collared dove
8 House sparrow
9 Pied wagtail
10 Pigs (Large white)
11 Farm dog
12 Wall pepper
13 Ivy
14 Ivy-leaved toadflax
15 House mouse
16 Feral cat
17 Alga
18 Liverwort
19 Pleurococcus
20 Shepherd's purse
21 Wall lizard
22 Hart's tongue fern
23 Cow parsley
24 Crottle, a lichen
25 White dead nettle
26 Common toad
27 Broad-leaved willowherb
28 Wall brown butterfly
29 Hedge garlic
30 Knot grass
31 Lesser burdock
32 Hedgehog
33 Coltsfoot
34 Buff Orpington hen
35 Dandelion
36 Germander speedwell
37 Pineapple weed
38 Brown rat
39 Pipistrelle bat

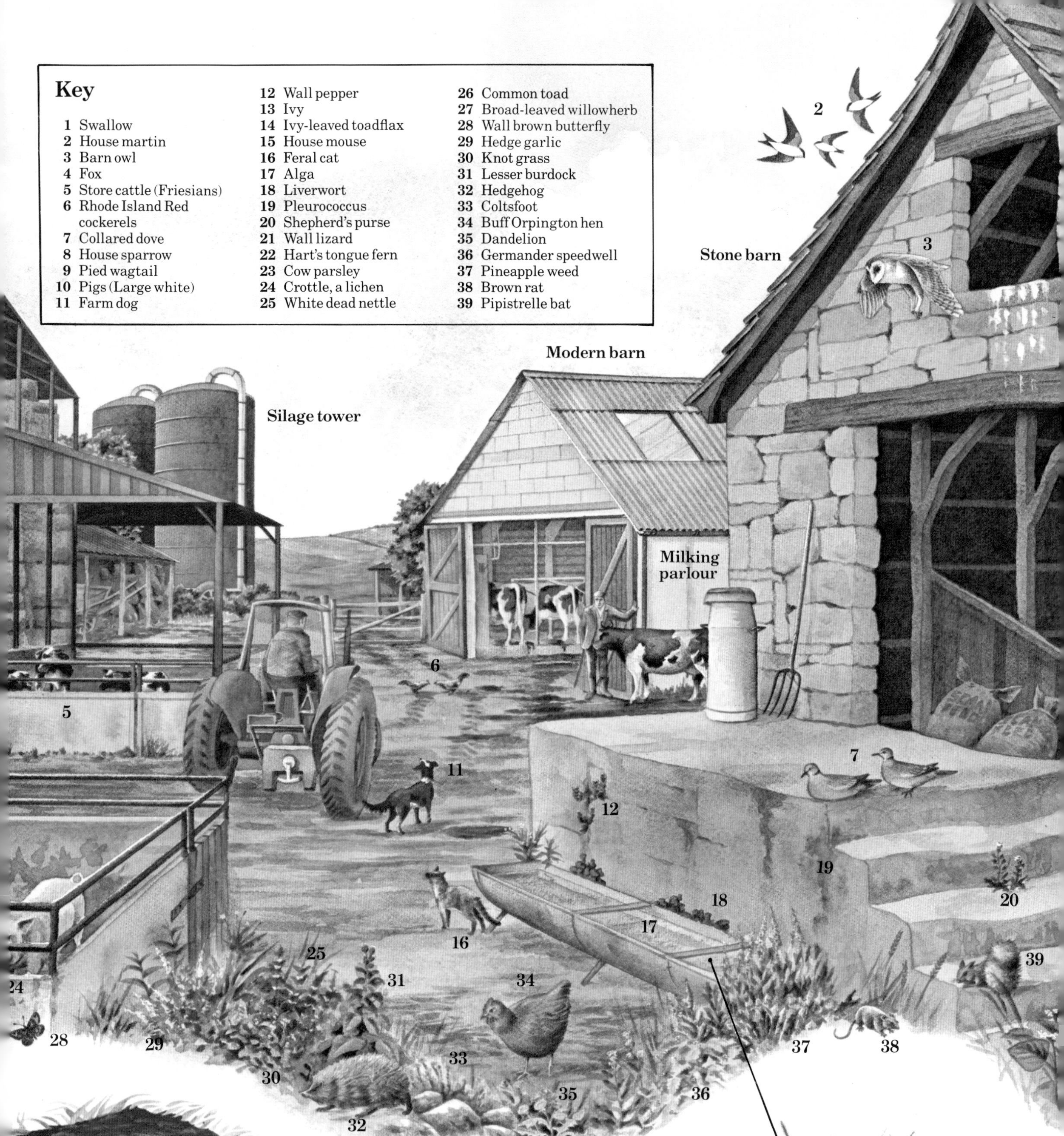

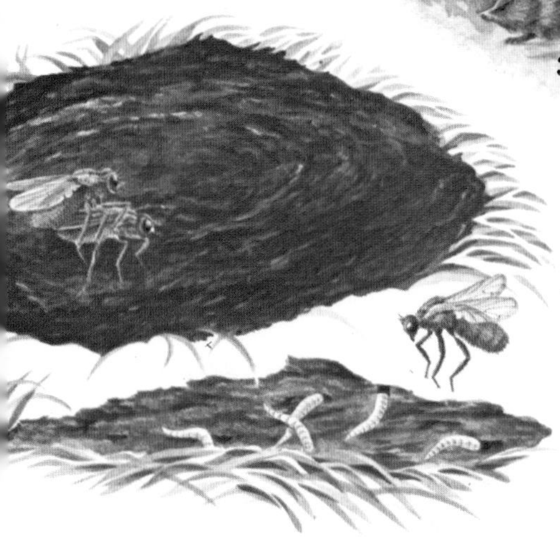

Stone barn
Modern barn
Silage tower
Milking parlour
2
3
5
6
7
11
12
16
17
18
19
20
24
25
28
29
30
31
32
33
34
35
36
37
38
39

► The life-cycle of the mosquito
Tiny rafts of eggs (**1**) are laid on still water. They hatch into wriggling larvae (**2**). These are filter-feeders, and breathe air through a 'siphon'. The comma-shaped pupae (**3**) have two siphons. The adult (**4**) emerges from the pupal case after a few days. Only the female sucks blood.

4
1
Siphon
2
3

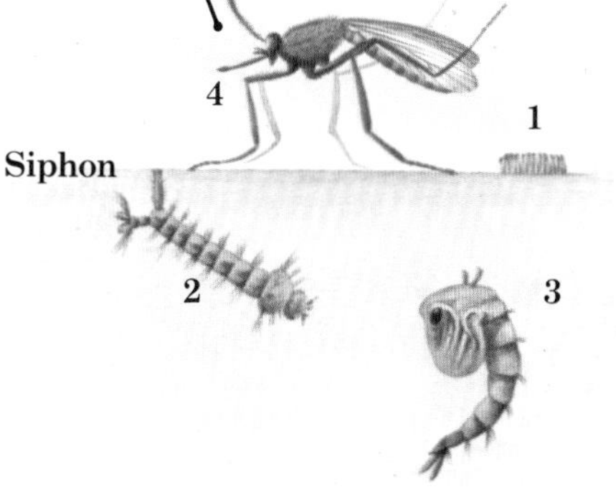

Wild flowers

Wild plants are called weeds when they grow in places where they are a nuisance to people, such as amongst crops. They compete with crops for minerals, water and light. If they are not removed they may affect the growth of crop plants.

Many of the wild plants on ploughed land are annuals. They grow quickly, often producing enormous numbers of tiny, light seeds which may survive in the soil for years.

* Not to scale. Average height given.

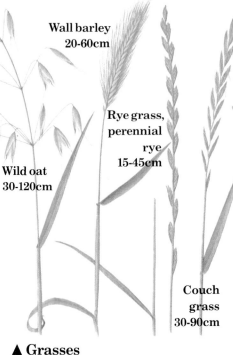

Wild oat
30-120cm

Wall barley
20-60cm

Rye grass,
perennial
rye
15-45cm

Couch
grass
30-90cm

▲ Grasses
These four grasses are found on cultivated land. Wild oat and couch are a serious problem amongst cereal crops. If not removed their seeds will be harvested with the crop. They can cause even greater problems when the seeds from that crop are sown. Wall barley and rye grass are more common in grassy waste places, by walls and near farm buildings.

▲ Toad rush 5-30cm (left)
Jointed rush 30-60cm (right)
Rushes are grass-like plants which grow in badly drained places. Unlike grasses their flowers have sepals and petals.

Toad rush is common along farm tracks and around ponds. The larger, jointed rush is common in wet meadows.

▲ Ribwort plantain 10-25cm
Common on grassland, banks and verges. Look for the long pointed leaves, ribbed underneath. The flowers have pale yellow anthers hanging out.

▲ Prickly sowthistle 20-150cm
A common annual weed. The leaves have prickly edges. Clusters of small dandelion-like flowers appear in midsummer.

▲ Charlock 30-80cm (left)
Common vetch 15-20cm (right)
Two annual weeds, common amongst crops, in waste places and on roadsides. Charlock uses up important minerals. If it grows amongst cereal crops they may not develop well.

Common vetch is a straggling climber. Notice the grasping tendrils and tiny fruits.

▲ Common hemp nettle 20-80cm (left) **Common ragwort** 30-120cm (right)
Both are common in waste places and on roadsides. Hemp nettle also grows on arable land. Its flowers vary from pink to yellow or white.

The yellow, daisy-like flowers of ragwort are commonly seen in sandy and chalky places. It also grows on grazing land.

▲ Ground elder 30-60cm
This creeping weed is common in shady places, near buildings, on wasteground and on roadsides. Its clusters of white flowers attract flies and beetles.

▲ Corn poppy 20-60cm
Grows in waste places, on roadsides, on disturbed ground and in fields. From May to August its beautiful flowers are common in cornfields.

▲ Shepherd's purse 35cm (left)
Fat hen up to 100cm (right)
Two very common weeds of waste places and cultivated land. The stems of fat hen may have red streaks, and its young shoots look floury. Shepherd's purse flowers throughout the year. Its seed pods look like the purses once carried by shepherds.

▲ Common toadflax 30-60cm
The bright yellow flower spikes of this perennial plant are a common sight from June to October in fields, hedgerows and waste places.

▲ Chickweed 35cm (left)
Groundsel 40cm (right)
Very common annual weeds of roadsides, waste land and cultivated ground. They both flower all the year round. These are amongst the first weeds to appear on newly-turned soil.

▲ Wall speedwell 20cm
A tiny plant, common on dry cultivated ground and grassland. It has toothed leaves and hairy stems, with tiny blue flowers.

▲ Coltsfoot 5-15cm
The small flowers appear in spring, long before the leaves develop. Common on hard, bare ground, especially on clay soils.

How farm flowers compete for survival

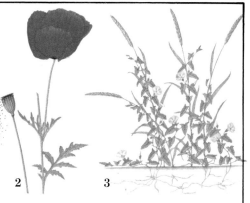

1. Couch grass spreads rapidly by underground stems. **2.** The tiny, light seeds of poppies are easily spread by the wind. **3.** Bindweed twines round the stems of plants to reach the light.

Chalk downs

The Downs are natural chalk uplands. They are found mainly in southern Britain. Here, Neolithic people began to farm with flint tools about 5,000 years ago. Many different chalk-loving plants grow amongst the short, fine grass, in the shallow, well-drained soil.

The commonest downland grasses are sheep's fescue and red fescue (26). The grass is kept short by the grazing of rabbits, hares (11) and sheep. Quaking grass (6) has delicate straggling branches that rustle in the wind. Common chalk-loving plants are small scabious (27), carline thistle (16) and yarrow (14).

Many different snails live here. They need the chalk to make strong shells. Heath snails (43) feed on salad burnet (34). Its leaves taste like cucumber.

The bloody-nosed beetle (23) defends itself by giving out a drop of nasty-smelling fluid from its mouth. The bright red liquid looks just like a drop of blood.

Many kinds of butterfly breed on chalkland. The larvae of the chalkhill blue (35) feed on bird's-foot trefoil (36). The caterpillars of the large blue (25) prefer the leaves of wild thyme (28). The day-flying six-spot burnet moth (19) lays its eggs on vetches (29) and trefoils (36).

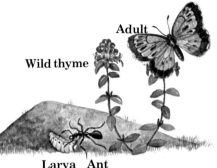

Adult
Wild thyme
Larva   Ant

▲ Glow worms
Glow worms are actually small beetles. The female has no wings. At night, during the mating season, she produces a pale yellow-green light from a special organ on her abdomen. This attracts the winged male.

▶ Rosette plants
The leaves of these plants grow in a flat circle called a rosette. The stems are very short, and the leaves lie flat against the ground. These plants are less likely to be damaged by grazing animals.

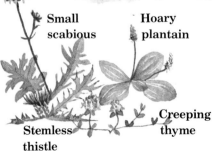

Small scabious

Hoary plantain

Stemless thistle

Creeping thyme

▶ Yellow meadow ants
The grass-covered mounds on downland are the nests of meadow ants. They feed on the honey dew produced by aphids, which they milk, like cattle. They keep the aphid eggs in their nests in winter. In spring the newly-hatched aphids are put out to 'graze'.

128

◀ **Large blue butterfly**

The caterpillars feed on wild thyme, then start to produce a sweet liquid from glands halfway down their bodies. This attracts certain kinds of ants, which carry the caterpillars to their nests and feed on the liquid. The caterpillars eat some of the ant larvae.

Key		
	14 Yarrow	30 Lesser knapweed
	15 Marbled white	31 Spiny restharrow
	16 Carline thistle	32 Grasshopper
1 Buzzard	17 Meadow pipit	33 Stone curlew
2 Skylark	18 Woody nightshade	34 Salad burnet
3 Whitebeam	19 Six-spot burnet moth	35 Chalkhill blue
4 Elder	20 Hoary plantain	36 Bird's-foot trefoil
5 Hawthorn	21 Shrew	37 Mouse-ear hawkweed
6 Quaking grass	22 Rock rose	38 Stemless thistle
7 Dog rose	23 Bloody-nosed beetle	39 Weasel
8 Yellowhammer	24 Wrinkled snail	40 Roman snail
9 Wheatear	25 Large blue	41 Pill woodlice
10 Swift	26 Red fescue	42 Violet ground beetle
11 Hares	27 Small scabious	43 Heath snail
12 Ant-hills	28 Wild thyme	44 Crested lark
13 Field vole	29 Horseshoe vetch	45 Dandelion

Farm animals

About 10,000 years ago people began to catch the young of wild cattle, and bred herds from them. Cattle provided meat to eat and skins for clothing. In Europe early farmers domesticated wild pigs and sheep, goats, poultry and rabbits in the same way. Today farmers try to breed animals which give the greatest amount of the best quality food in the shortest time. They are helped by genetics, the science of breeding.

* Not to scale.

▶ Cattle

There are over twenty breeds of cattle in Britain. Some are bred mainly for their milk. Friesians are the most common dairy cow. Jerseys produce very creamy milk. Milk from Ayrshires makes good cheese.

Cattle like the Hereford are bred for their meat, beef. The tough Highland cattle are found mostly in the Scottish mountains, where conditions are poor. The Devon is a dual-purpose cow, bred for milk and meat.

The male is called a bull and the female a cow. The young are calves.

▶ Sheep

There are three main types of sheep. Long-wool sheep produce poor quality meat, but up to 33kg of wool a year. The wool is used to make worsted cloth. Short-wool sheep have a short-haired fleece, usually spun into knitting wool. The most common sheep are the hill breeds. They are small, hardy sheep producing good mutton and up to 11kg of wool per year.

Male sheep are called rams and females, ewes. The young are called lambs.

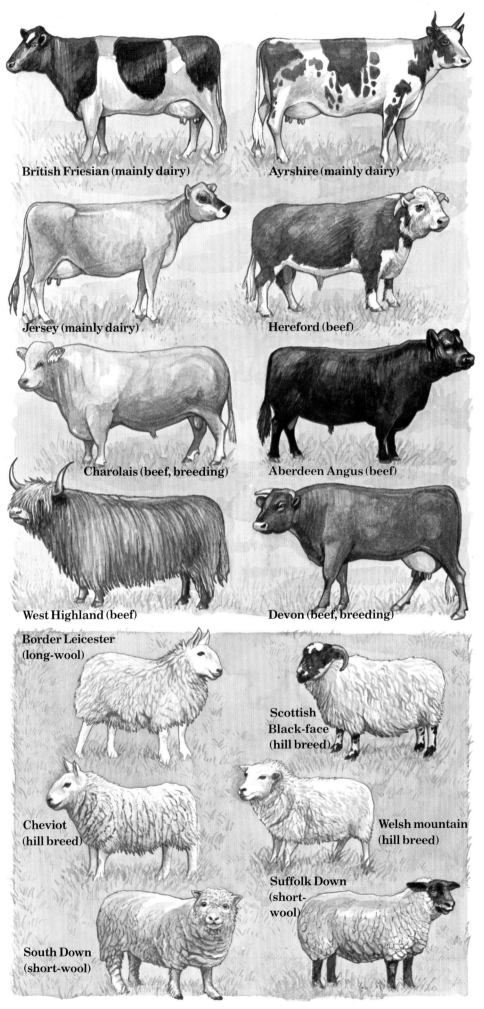

British Friesian (mainly dairy)

Ayrshire (mainly dairy)

Jersey (mainly dairy)

Hereford (beef)

Charolais (beef, breeding)

Aberdeen Angus (beef)

West Highland (beef)

Devon (beef, breeding)

Border Leicester (long-wool)

Scottish Black-face (hill breed)

Cheviot (hill breed)

Welsh mountain (hill breed)

Suffolk Down (short-wool)

South Down (short-wool)

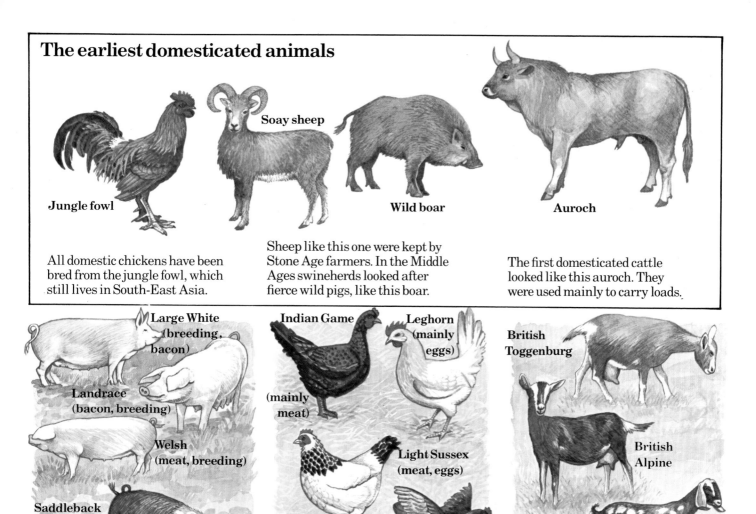

Jungle fowl

Soay sheep

Wild boar

Auroch

All domestic chickens have been bred from the jungle fowl, which still lives in South-East Asia.

Sheep like this one were kept by Stone Age farmers. In the Middle Ages swineherds looked after fierce wild pigs, like this boar.

The first domesticated cattle looked like this auroch. They were used mainly to carry loads.

Large White (breeding, bacon)

Landrace (bacon, breeding)

Welsh (meat, breeding)

Saddleback (meat, breeding)

Large Black (meat, breeding)

Indian Game (mainly meat)

Leghorn (mainly eggs)

Light Sussex (meat, eggs)

Wyandotte (meat, eggs)

Rhode Island Red (meat, eggs)

British Toggenburg

British Alpine

Anglo-Nubian

British Saanen

▲ Pigs

Pigs are thought to be the most intelligent, cleanest farm animals. They have large appetites and will eat almost anything.

Pigs are bred for their meat – pork, bacon and ham. The skins are used to make leather goods, and their bristly hair is made into brushes. Most pigs are kept in sties inside pig houses. The small sties restrict their movement, so they use up less energy, and fatten up more quickly.

Pigs breed quickly. After mating it takes only 16 weeks before the sow produces her litter of around 10 piglets. A sow can have more than two litters every year. The male pig is called a boar.

▲ Chickens

These chickens are the 'standard' breeds. They are no longer used for egg and meat production. However, they are often kept as free-range chickens.

Poultry farmers use 'hybrid' chickens. These are produced by mating together different kinds of standard breeds. Hybrids may produce better meat or more eggs.

The best hybrids are selected and bred for commercial use. The birds, mainly hens, are kept caged in windowless buildings called battery, or broiler, houses. The temperature, light and food are carefully controlled for maximum egg and meat production. Male chickens are called cockerels.

▲ Goats

Goats are kept mainly for their milk, which tastes different from cow's milk. It has smaller fat globules, which makes it easier to digest. The milk can be made into strong-flavoured cheese. In some countries goats are also kept for meat.

Goats will eat almost anything. They can do a great deal of damage to trees and hedges, so on farms they are usually tethered on chains. Goats survive well on pasture that is too poor for cattle or sheep.

A nanny goat can produce about 4½ litres of milk a day. The male, billy goats usually have beards, bad tempers and smell strongly. Young goats are called kids.

Farm crops

In natural habitats there are many different kinds of plants competing for survival. Crop fields are artificial habitats, in which usually only one kind of plant is grown at a time. As crop plants are grown close together plant pests can spread very quickly.

* Not to scale. Size depends on the crop variety and the way in which it is grown.

Key to main uses
H: Human consumption;
A: Animal food; **O:** Other uses
(eg industrial)

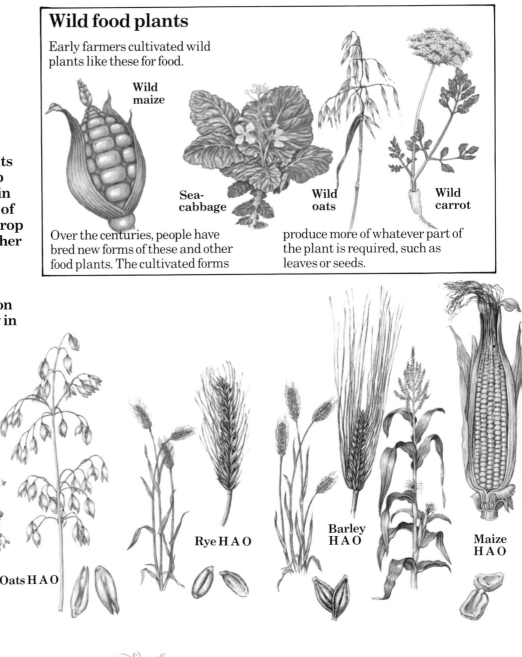

Wild food plants
Early farmers cultivated wild plants like these for food.

Wild maize

Sea-cabbage

Wild oats

Wild carrot

Over the centuries, people have bred new forms of these and other food plants. The cultivated forms produce more of whatever part of the plant is required, such as leaves or seeds.

Oats H A O

Rye H A O

Barley H A O

Maize H A O

Wheat H A (some)

▲ Cereals
Bread wheat is the most important and widely grown cereal. Oat flour helps to keep margarine and cake mixes fresh. The husks are used in making nylon and antiseptics. Rye straw is good for thatching and papermaking. 'Malted' barley is used in brewing. Maize is grown for fodder, silage and as a vegetable.

▶ Legumes
Peas and beans belong to the legume family. Bacteria living in nodules on the roots of these plants help to add nitrogen to the soil. Most pea and bean crops are grown for freezing, drying or canning. Field beans are grown for fodder.

Pea H A

Runner bean H A

Field bean A

132

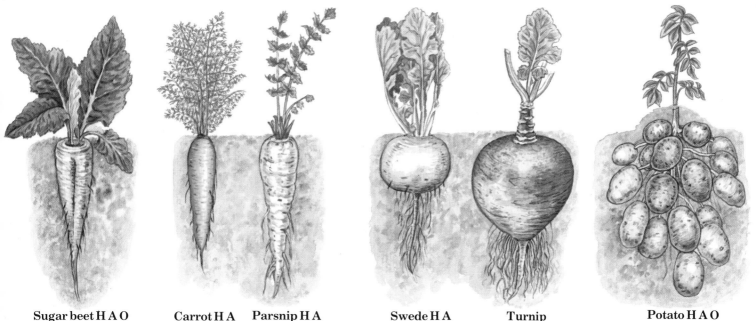

Sugar beet H A O   Carrot H A   Parsnip H A   Swede H A   Turnip   Potato H A O

▲ Root crops

About 40 per cent of the world's sugar is produced from sugar beet. Carrots, parsnips, turnips and swedes are grown for their swollen roots. Potatoes are the swollen ends of underground stems. The green parts of potatoes are poisonous.

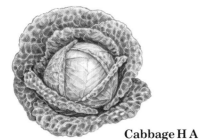

Cabbage H A

▲ The cabbage family

All these plants are closely related to the cabbage. Curly kale is a popular vegetable. Other varieties of kale are used as animal feed and in floral arrangements. Brussels sprouts are really miniature cabbages. We eat the young flowers of broccoli and cauliflower.

Kale H A O   Brussels sprouts H   Cauliflower H   Broccoli H

► Other common crops

Rape seed oil is used in cattle feed. Clover, lucerne (alfalfa) and rye grass are grown for hay, green cattle feed or silage. White mustard plants are fed to sheep or ploughed in as green manure. Table mustard is made by grinding black mustard seeds.

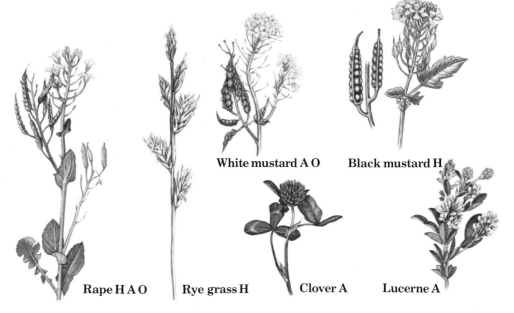

White mustard A O   Black mustard H

Rape H A O   Rye grass H   Clover A   Lucerne A

A mountain

Mountains may look beautiful in the sun, but the weather makes it very difficult to survive. Plants and animals have to be adapted to long periods of cold weather and snow, short summers and strong winds. Most plants are small and there are few big trees, except in sheltered valleys.

Mountain-tops

The stony mountain tops have a patchy cover of lichens and mosses. This bleak area is the summer home of dotterel (9) and snow buntings (22). Rock ledges make safe nesting places for golden eagles (5), peregrine falcons (1) and ravens (3). The peregrine catches pigeons by swooping down on them at an incredible speed.

▼ Money spider

Taller plants, such as greater woodrush and meadowsweet, can grow on sheltered, ungrazed rock ledges. Many tiny animals live among the leaves, like this money spider. It spins a sheet web to catch small flies.

Plants and tiny animals

Many different flowers grow on richer mountain soils. Creeping azalea (31) forms mats. Cushions of moss campion (26) and purple saxifrage (14), and rosettes of mountain avens (28) grow behind rocks, out of the wind. Dwarf birch (12) and willow (25) provide food for the alpine saw-fly (11). Ground beetles (30) hunt for springtails (32).

Key

1 Peregrine falcon
2 Feral pigeon
3 Raven
4 Hooded crow
5 Golden eagle
6 Red deer
7 Wild cat's lair
8 Mountain goat
9 Dotterel
10 Ptarmigan
11 Alpine saw-fly
12 Dwarf birch
13 Small mountain ringlet butterfly
14 Purple saxifrage
15 Red-throated diver
16 Juniper
17 Cranefly
18 Cottongrass
19 Mountain hare
20 Heather
21 Bilberry
22 Snow bunting
23 Bogmoss
24 Mountain burnet moth
25 Dwarf willow
26 Moss campion
27 Mountain sedge
28 Mountain avens
29 Woolly hair moss
30 Ground beetle
31 Creeping azalea
32 Springtail
33 Lichen

Red deer

Red deer hinds (6) graze over the lower slopes in summer, while the stags stay higher up. Stags' antlers usually fall off in spring. New ones grow at once. They are covered in soft skin called velvet. When the antlers are fully formed, the velvet is rubbed off on trees or bushes. They will be used for the rut in the autumn.

Ptarmigan (10)

These are the mountain grouse. The males occupy territories as soon as the snow melts. They defend them with fights, aerial chases and long boundary walks alongside intruders.

◄ Cranefly

This insect is often called a daddy-long-legs. There are many types. The female (shown here) has a thin tube-like egg-laying organ at the end of the body. After mating, she lays hundreds of eggs in wet peat.

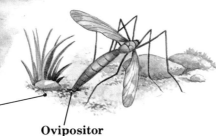

Ovipositor

▼ Palmate newt

This is the only British newt which lives in high-level peaty pools. The male has a tiny hair-like extension on the tip of its tail. The eggs are wrapped in leaves to protect them from predators.

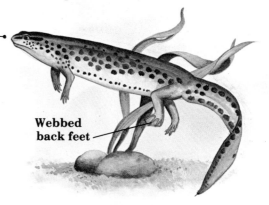

Webbed back feet

135

Birds

There are not as many different birds on heaths, moors or mountains as in woodlands. However, there are often large numbers of one particular bird, such as the meadow pipit. Few stay throughout the winter because of the bad weather and lack of food. Some migrate to other countries, while others move to the lowlands or coasts to feed.

* Not to scale. Average body-length given.

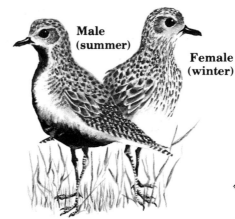

Male (summer)

Female (winter)

▲ **Golden plover** 28cm
A beautiful gold and black bird, which breeds on moors, and winters in flocks in fields or estuaries. When they have eggs or chicks, the birds pretend to have damaged wings to distract predators.

▲ **Skylark** 17·5cm
This is the only British bird which sings while flying up, hovering and descending again. The singing defends its territory and attracts a mate. It nests on grasslands, moors and bogs where there are no trees.

▲ **Dartford warbler** 12·5cm
This bird lives on heaths, mainly in France and Spain. After the severe 1962–3 winter, there were only 10 pairs in Britain. There are now over 100 pairs. They breed in gorse or tall heather and feed on insects.

Female

Male

▲ **Whinchat** 12cm
The whinchat is one of the earliest summer visitors to return from Africa. It breeds on moors, heaths and rough grassland, and sings from gorse, bracken or thistles. It feeds on insects and larvae.

Male

Female

▲ **Hen harrier** 42cm (female bigger)
This bird glides low over moors, and then pounces to seize a mouse, frog, bird chick or egg. The nest is built on the ground in tall heather, and 4 white eggs are laid in May or June.

Male

Female

Chick

Nest

◄ **Red grouse** 36cm (female smaller)
This bird only lives in Britain. The similar willow grouse lives in northern Europe. Grouse live on heather moors, and feed on the shoots of heather and bilberry. The chicks eat some insects.

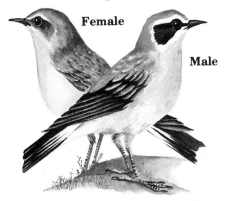

Female

Male

▲ **Carrion crow** (right)
Hooded crow (left) 46cm
Notice that the hooded crow has
a grey body. It only lives in
Scotland and Ireland. Both
crows feed on fruit, birds' eggs,
chicks and dead animals. They
nest on rock ledges or in trees.

▶ **Raven** 63cm
This large, black bird has a
stout bill, shaggy throat and
wedge-shaped tail. Its call is a
low croak. It feeds on dead
animals, birds' eggs and small
animals on mountains and
moors. It nests on rock ledges.

▲ **Wheatear** 15cm
This bird chases insects on the
ground and nests in rocky
hillsides or drystone walls. Male
wheatears 'dance', to attract
mates, when they reach their
breeding sites after flying from
Africa.

▲ **Meadow pipit** 14cm
This small, brown bird sings
while it glides, like a parachute,
on to a mound or heather. It is
common on moors, mountains,
heaths and grasslands. It eats
tiny animals. Cuckoos often lay
eggs in its nest.

▲ **Common gull** 42·5cm
This bird is not as common as
herring or black-headed gulls. It
often nests in small colonies on
moors, bogs and islands in lochs,
mostly in Scotland. In winter it
lives round coasts and towns,
scavenging for food.

▲ **Nightjar** 27cm
The nightjar hides in dead
leaves in daytime, camouflaged
by its markings. It flies at
sunset, twisting and turning to
catch moths. Its name comes
from the sound it makes.

Bird feet

**The feet of birds are
adapted to their way of life.**

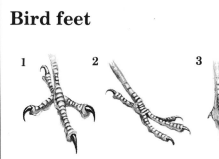

1   2   3   4   5

1. The peregrine falcon has sharp
claws to hold and kill prey.
2. The linnet has three toes in front
and one curled behind, for perching.
3. The common gull has three webbed
toes for paddling.
4. The curlew has long toes, which

spread out to stop it sinking in soft
mud.
5. The ptarmigan has thick feathers
to keep its legs free of snow. Its long,
wide claws dig out food plants, and the
scales on its toes stop it sinking into
the snow.

Moorland

Vast stretches of hills are covered with heather moorland. But heather is not the only plant growing here. Mosses and lichens live underneath its shrubby stems. On the deeper peat there are some of the plants of the peat bog, like cottongrasses. Bilberry and cowberry bushes spread out on the dry edges.

In the steep-sided valleys there are a few trees. They cling to the rock outcrops and fringe the streams. Small springs and damp areas line these valleys, and it is here that most plants grow.

▼ Waterlife

Most of the stream's small animals live under stones, away from the fast-flowing water. The nymphs (young stages) of the stoneflies and mayflies are hunted by the dipper (28). The black-fly larvae are protected in their silken cases, while the flatworm is hidden under stones where it feeds on small animals. The tiny, pale shrimps swim on their sides between the stones.

Tiny animals

Under the heather and bilberry there is great activity. The moorland carpet moth (30) lays its eggs on heather. The male of the emperor moth (20) flies during the day, seeking the female by following her scent. She also lays her eggs on heather. Heather beetles (39) can be so numerous that they eat whole plants. Spiders (33) and ground beetles (40) track or catch their prey among the stems.

Birds

The most common small moorland bird is the meadow pipit (2). It lays grey-brown eggs in grassy nests. Sometimes the cuckoo (11) finds a meadow pipit's nest and lays its own egg in it. The young cuckoo pushes out the pipit's eggs or young. The merlin (1) dashes along close to the heather, twisting and turning to catch meadow pipits. It will also chase ring-ouzels (6). They are summer visitors, which breed in moorland valleys. The buzzard (3) is looking for bigger prey, such as rabbits.

Grouse droppings

▲ Grouse droppings and dung beetles

Grouse droppings are left in neat little piles. They are like slim, brown cigarette ends with cream streaks. You can see undigested bits of heather and bilberry stems in them. The droppings are eaten by dung beetles and their larvae.

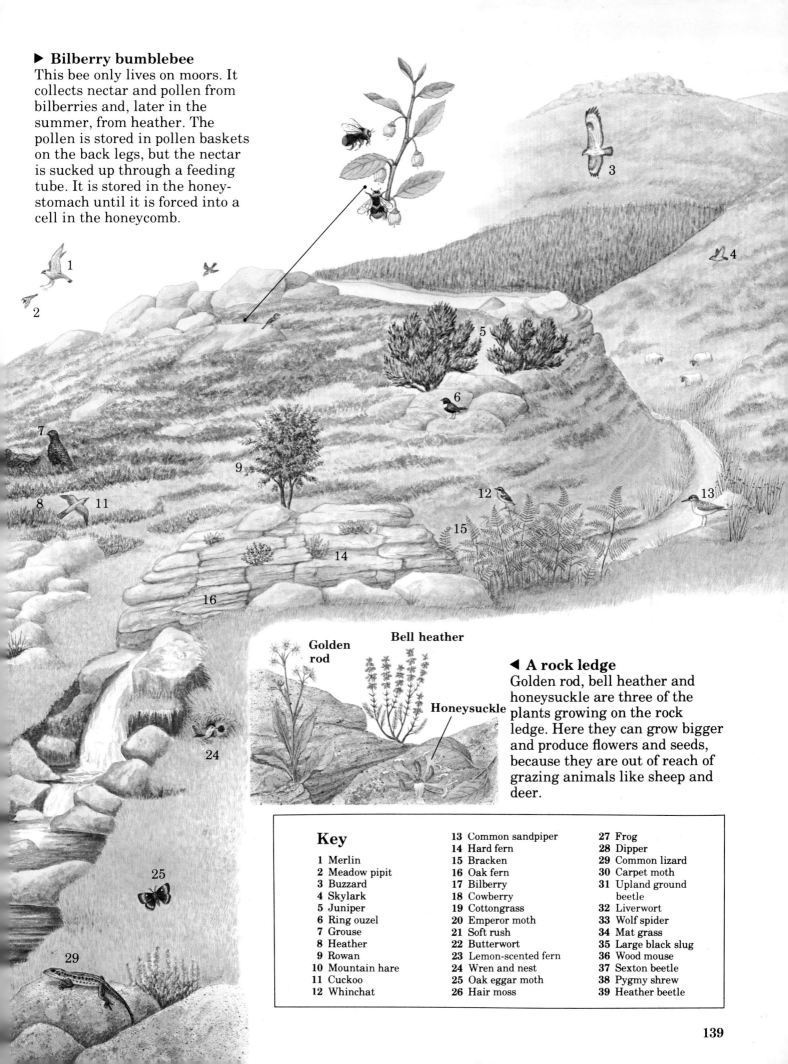

▶ **Bilberry bumblebee**
This bee only lives on moors. It collects nectar and pollen from bilberries and, later in the summer, from heather. The pollen is stored in pollen baskets on the back legs, but the nectar is sucked up through a feeding tube. It is stored in the honey-stomach until it is forced into a cell in the honeycomb.

Golden rod

Bell heather

Honeysuckle

◀ **A rock ledge**
Golden rod, bell heather and honeysuckle are three of the plants growing on the rock ledge. Here they can grow bigger and produce flowers and seeds, because they are out of reach of grazing animals like sheep and deer.

Key

1 Merlin	13 Common sandpiper
2 Meadow pipit	14 Hard fern
3 Buzzard	15 Bracken
4 Skylark	16 Oak fern
5 Juniper	17 Bilberry
6 Ring ouzel	18 Cowberry
7 Grouse	19 Cottongrass
8 Heather	20 Emperor moth
9 Rowan	21 Soft rush
10 Mountain hare	22 Butterwort
11 Cuckoo	23 Lemon-scented fern
12 Whinchat	24 Wren and nest
	25 Oak eggar moth
	26 Hair moss

27 Frog
28 Dipper
29 Common lizard
30 Carpet moth
31 Upland ground beetle
32 Liverwort
33 Wolf spider
34 Mat grass
35 Large black slug
36 Wood mouse
37 Sexton beetle
38 Pygmy shrew
39 Heather beetle

Trees and shrubs

Tall trees cannot grow on mountain tops because of the strong winds, snow and cold. They are more common on rock ledges and on heathland. Smaller, bushy, slow-growing shrubs are common on moors, mountains and heathland.

* Not to scale. The average height is given.

▲ **Bearberry** up to 1m
Bearberry forms a mat of dark-green evergreen leaves. The lower surface of each leaf is covered with a net-like pattern. The strongly-scented, pale pink flowers attract bumblebees. It is common on moors and mountains.

▲ **Bell heather** up to 60cm
The small, narrow leaves are grouped in threes on the stem. The dark pink, bell-shaped flowers are larger than heather flowers. Bell heather grows in small bushes on dry heaths and moorland slopes.

▲ **Crowberry** 15–45cm
An evergreen, mat-like shrub which is common on high moors and mountains. The black berry tastes very sharp and should not be eaten. It has to pass through the stomach of a bird before it will grow.

▲ **Dwarf willow**
This is a tiny mountain tree with twigs only 2 to 3cm high. It spreads to form a mat. The female and male flowers grow on separate plants. The catkins have nectaries, which attract insects for pollination.

▲ **Common gorse** 60–200cm
A bush with spiny leaves, which grows on heathland and acid grassland. It has flowers throughout the year. Sheep graze on the bush, especially in spring when the spines are young and soft.

▲ **Bog myrtle** 60–90cm
Rub your finger on the leaves and you will find they have a lovely resin-like smell. The male and female catkins are on separate plants. Bog myrtle grows in bogs and on wet moors.

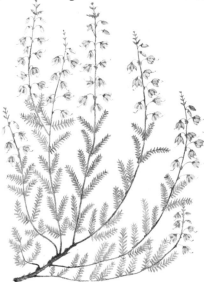

▲ **Heather** up to 60cm
Masses of tiny heather flowers turn dry moors and heaths pink in late summer. Heather honey is made by bees from hives which have been put out on heaths and moors. Heather was used to thatch cottage roofs.

▲ **Creeping azalea**
A very pretty plant which forms a low mat on mountain tops. The tiny, bright pink flowers appear in summer. The dark green leaves grow in pairs opposite each other. Their edges are rolled under to stop water loss.

▲ **Cowberry** up to 30cm
The dark, shiny leaves have tiny dots on the lower surface, which are oil glands. The red berry is too sharp for us to eat, but many birds like them. This grows on moorland and heaths.

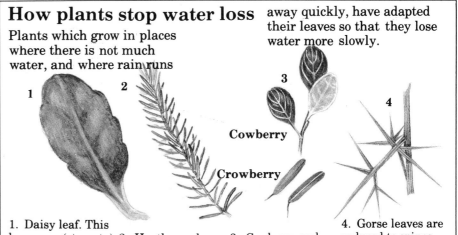

How plants stop water loss

Plants which grow in places where there is not much water, and where rain runs away quickly, have adapted their leaves so that they lose water more slowly.

Cowberry

Crowberry

1. Daisy leaf. This has pores (stomata) on both surfaces, and no thick, waxy covering. It cannot grow in dry places.

2. Heather reduces the number of stomata by having very small leaves.

3. Cowberry and crowberry leaves have thick leathery, waxy upper surfaces to stop water loss.

4. Gorse leaves are reduced to spines. The green stems also make food, since the surface of the spines is so small.

▲ **Cranberry**
Narrow, dark green leaves grow on long stems, which trail across bogs. Pretty pink flowers appear in June. They produce red berries, which can be made into sauce, though American berries are more often used.

▲ **Cornish heath**
This plant grows on the Lizard heaths in Cornwall, and on French heaths. You can distinguish it from heather by its longer flower stalks, larger, pale pink, bell-shaped flowers and bushier appearance.

▲ **Cross-leaved heath** up to 60cm
Small, narrow, greyish-green leaves grow in fours, forming cross-shapes along the stem. The pale pink or, sometimes, white flowers grow at the top of the stem. This plant grows in damp, peaty areas.

▲ **Dwarf birch** up to 100cm
This tree has round, toothed leaves, and small catkins in the summer. Wind blows the pollen from male to female flowers, which grow on the same tree. It grows on mountains, and is rare in Britain.

◄ **Juniper** up to 3m
In sheltered areas of moorland and grassland this shrub grows as a prickly, upright bush. On mountain tops it forms a softer, flattened, mat-like bush. The seeds are in small cones.

Butterflies and moths

Butterflies and moths are insects with scaly wings. They lay eggs which develop into caterpillars. The caterpillars turn into adults inside a pupa, or cocoon. Most butterflies fly in the daytime. Some upland moths do too, because the nights can be very cold.

▲ **Grey mountain carpet moth** 12mm: Ws 30mm
This is a common mottled brown moth of moors and mountains. The caterpillar hibernates in winter and feeds in late spring on bilberry or heather. The moth emerges from its pupa in summer.

▲ **Map-winged swift moth** 17mm: Ws 40mm
The brownish wing markings look rather like a map. This moth flies at dusk on hills, heaths and bogs in summer. Its caterpillar is one of the few animals which can feed on bracken roots.

▲ **Smoky wave moth** 9mm: Ws 23mm
You may see this moth in June and July flying over moors and bogs, in the north and west. Both the male and the female are greyish-white with pale markings. The caterpillars feed on bilberry, heather or goat willow.

▲ **Drinker moth** 23mm: Ws 55mm
A large, furry-looking orange moth which lives in moors, marshes and damp grassy places. Its name comes from the caterpillar's habit of drinking drops of dew. The caterpillars feed on grasses.

▲ **Grass moth** 10mm: Ws 21–25mm
The front wings are brown with a white central line. The back or hind wings are paler. The wings are folded round the body when resting. This is a nocturnal moth of moors and heaths. The caterpillar feeds on grasses.

▲ **Fox moth** 27mm: Ws 63mm (male smaller)
The male fox moth flies in daylight over heaths and moors, searching for females, in May or June. The large hairy caterpillars, which feed on heather, can give you a rash.

▲ **Vapourer moth** 12mm: Ws male only 32mm
The female has a tubby body but no wings. She attracts the male to her by producing a strong scent. The moth is common on heather, as well as on trees and bushes.

▲ **Antler moth** 14mm: Ws 28–32mm
The pale markings on the wings look like a stag's antlers. Male moths fly by day over grassland moors, and suck nectar from flowers like thistles. The caterpillars feed on grasses.

142

▲ Small heath butterfly
10mm: Ws 30mm
This small butterfly is very common on heaths and grasslands. It also lives quite high on mountains. The first eggs are laid in May, and can become butterflies by August.

▲ Large heath butterfly
12mm: Ws 35mm
The large heath is common on mountains and bogs. The caterpillars feed on white-beaked sedge, which grows on wet peat. The butterfly is on the wing in June and July.

▲ Brown argus butterfly
10mm: Ws 26mm (left). **Cistus forester moth** 7mm: Ws 20mm (right)
Both of these insects live on limestone grasslands. Their caterpillars eat rockrose. The caterpillar of the cistus forester burrows into a leaf when it hatches, then gradually eats the rest of the leaf.

▲ Mountain ringlet butterfly
11mm: Ws 34mm
This butterfly is a true mountain species, and is not found below 600m. The dark brown wings are marked by an orange band or spots, with small black dots. The caterpillars feed on grasses, especially mat grass.

▲ Green hairstreak butterfly
9mm: Ws 25mm
The undersides of the golden-brown wings are green. You may see the butterflies flying in May and June over heaths and grasslands. The caterpillars feed on rockrose, gorse or bilberry in June and July.

▲ Common blue butterfly
11mm: Ws 27mm
Only the male is blue. The female is brown with some blue scales. The caterpillar feeds on bird's-foot trefoil. This butterfly is common on grasslands.

The balance of numbers

Each pair of oak eggar moths lays many eggs. But only two survive.

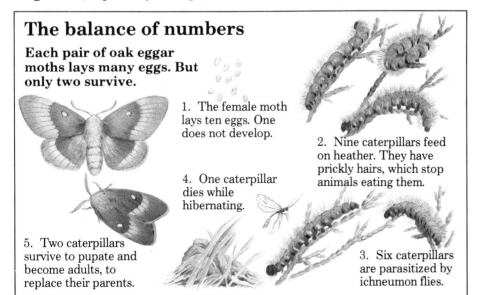

1. The female moth lays ten eggs. One does not develop.

2. Nine caterpillars feed on heather. They have prickly hairs, which stop animals eating them.

4. One caterpillar dies while hibernating.

5. Two caterpillars survive to pupate and become adults, to replace their parents.

3. Six caterpillars are parasitized by ichneumon flies.

▲ Moorland clouded yellow
18mm: Ws 52mm
This butterfly is found on moors and bogs in northern Europe, but not in Britain, in June and July. Its yellowish wings have a dark margin. The caterpillars feed on bilberry.

Flowering plants

The flowering herbs (plants with no hard, woody growth) are more common on grasslands and mountains. There are fewer on the moors and heaths, where the soil is less fertile. Instead, shrubs like heather are widespread.

* Not to scale. Average height given.

▲ **Globe flower** 10–40cm
This looks rather like a large buttercup, but has twice as many pale yellow petals. The leaves are a shiny dark green. It grows in damp pastures and lime-rich areas in mountains. It is poisonous, so grazing animals avoid it.

▲ **Starry saxifrage** 5–20cm
This plant grows on mountains by streams, in springs and on wet rock ledges. It forms a small rosette of thick leaves. The flowers are white, with bright orange-red anthers.

▲ **Alpine meadow-rue** 8–12cm (right) **Alpine lady's mantle** 10–20cm (left)
This meadow-rue grows on rock ledges. The flowers have no petals. The pollen is blown by the wind to nearby female flowers.

The under-surface of each leaf of alpine lady's mantle is covered in silvery-grey hairs, which help to stop water loss. The plant grows on dry rocky areas, and windy grasslands in mountains.

▲ **Mat grass** 10–30cm
Mat grass grows in tufts of wiry, greyish-green leaves, which are bleached white by the sun in summer. The flowers all grow on one side of the stem. Mat grass can cover whole hillsides on acid, peaty soils.

▲ **Mountain everlasting** 5–15cm
The small, hairy leaves grow in rosettes on rocks in lime-rich grassland and on mountains. The hairs help to stop water loss in windy places. The male and female flowers grow on separate plants.

▲ **Bird's-foot trefoil** 10–30cm (top) **Thyme** (bottom)
The flowers of bird's-foot trefoil develop into long, thin seed-pods, which look like a bird's foot. This plant is common on lime-rich grassland.

Thyme forms a low mat on dry heaths and among rocks. Its leaves smell pleasant. The flowers attract bees.

◄ Deer grass 10–35cm
This is not a true grass but a type of sedge. Its bright green stems grow in tufts, which can cover peaty hillsides. The dark brown flowers are perched at the tips of the stems.

▲ **Lousewort** 8–20cm (right)
Heath spotted orchid 15–50cm (left)
Lousewort is a small plant which grows in peaty places. It is partly parasitic on other plants, mostly grasses. It takes some food from the grass roots, so needs fewer leaves to make its own.

This orchid has a rosette of green leaves with black blotches. It grows amongst heather on damp peat, and in wetter boggy areas.

▲ **Melancholy thistle**
45–100cm
The leaves are white and felty underneath, green above, and have no prickles. Most of them are oval-shaped, with a toothed edge. Each plant has many beautiful purple flower-heads. It grows in northern grasslands and mountains.

▲ **Common cottongrass**
20–50cm (right) **Hare's-tail cottongrass** 20–40cm (left)
The 'cotton' describes the silky seed-heads. The leaves of common cottongrass are wide, and turn red in autumn. This plant grows as single stems in peaty pools.

Each stem of hare's-tail cottongrass has only one seedhead. The wiry, pale leaves grow in tussocks, which can cover large areas of wet peaty moorland. These two plants often grow together.

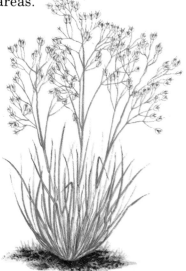

▲ **Wavy-hair grass** 20–30cm
The fine, dark-green leaves grow in tufts amongst heather and bilberry on moor and heath. Its name comes from the delicate, wavy stems of the flowerheads. Deer and sheep eat this grass.

Short cuts in reproduction

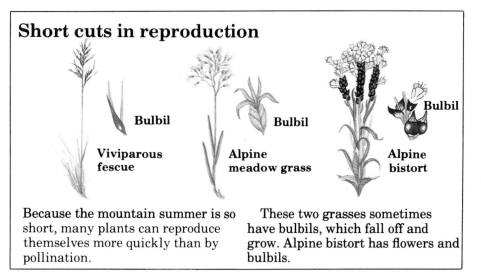

Viviparous fescue — Bulbil

Alpine meadow grass — Bulbil

Alpine bistort — Bulbil

Because the mountain summer is so short, many plants can reproduce themselves more quickly than by pollination.

These two grasses sometimes have bulbils, which fall off and grow. Alpine bistort has flowers and bulbils.

Heathland

Heathland is a surprisingly varied habitat. Much of it looks very similar, particularly where there is a wide expanse of heather. But if you look closely, you will see many different plants and animals in different places. The insects which scurry around on the bare sandy places are not the same as those in the wet boggy bits. Some heaths have trees, patches of gorse and bracken. There are different birds and insects in each.

Moss: Hypnum cuppressiforme

Lichen: Cladonia coccifera

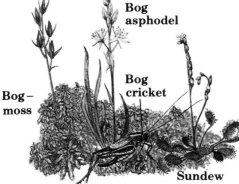

Bog asphodel

Bog cricket

Bog–moss

Sundew

◀ The bog
The sundew catches small flies in sticky drops on its leaf hairs. After the plant has digested the inside of the fly, the hard parts blow away.

The noisy bog bush cricket lives among bogmosses, bog asphodel and cross-leaved heath, and catches small insects.

Boggy places
Adders (17) like to bask on tussocks of purple moor grass (13) in the sun before going off to hunt for birds' eggs or mice. The golden-winged dragonfly (7) hunts for insects over wetter, boggy areas.

Gorse bushes
make safe homes for many animals. Linnets (26) and stonechats (15) hide their nests inside a bush. The rare red-backed shrike (6) sticks bees on to prickles. It will eat them later. Bees and moths visit the flowers and caterpillars of the green hairstreak butterfly (29) feed on the spines.

◀ **An old heather plant**
It is dark and humid under heather plants. Here you will find spiders and beetles hunting in the mosses for small insects. As the plant grows older, the branches spread out. This lets in more light to the ground below. New plants can grow underneath, like the red-tipped lichen on the left, and the stag's horn clubmoss in the centre.

Key

1 Skylark
2 Scot's pine
3 Silver birch
4 Oak
5 Bell heather
6 Red-backed shrike
7 Golden-winged dragonfly
8 Cross-leaved heath
9 Hare's-tail cottongrass
10 Hair moss
11 Bogmoss
12 Bilberry
13 Purple moor grass
14 Gorse
15 Stonechat
16 Map-winged swift moth
17 Adder
18 Dartford warbler
19 Green hairstreak butterfly
20 Bracken
21 Heath bedstraw
22 Tormentil
23 Wavy hair grass
24 Grayling butterfly
25 Sand lizard
26 Linnet
27 Honey bee
28 Nightjar
29 Green hairstreak caterpillar
30 Bilberry
31 Heath bumblebee
32 Small heath butterfly
33 Mining bee
34 Sheep's fescue
35 Minotaur beetle
36 Ants
37 Grasshopper

▲ **Ants**
Ant colonies are scattered all over the heathland. Each colony defends an area of about 40 square metres. Workers attack, kill and eat invading ants from other areas. The nest is deep, so that the ants can survive fires and cold weather.

Dry, sandy places
Red ants build nests in small mounds. Rabbits often leave their droppings on these mounds. The female minotaur beetle (35) digs a hole, and the male rolls in a rabbit dropping. The eggs are laid in the dung. When the larvae hatch they feed on it.

Smaller plants grow near the path, where there is no heather. The grayling butterfly (24) feeds on tormentil (22) and heath bedstraw (21). The caterpillars of this butterfly feed on grasses, like wavy hair grass (23). The mottled grasshopper rubs its hind legs against a hard part of the front wings to 'sing'. The female (37) lays her eggs in the soft sand.

Large animals

Most of the larger animals can be seen in daylight on heaths, moors or mountains. You will need to move quietly or sit and wait, since many animals are shy and nervous of people.

* Not to scale. Average body-length given.

▲ **Mountain, blue hare** 52cm
It has shorter ears and a whiter tail than the brown hare. It lives on moors in Scotland, Ireland, North Wales and the Peak District, but is more widespread in northern Europe. It feeds on heather and cottongrasses.

▲ **Wild cat** 56cm; tail 30cm
This is like a large tabby with a bushy, ringed tail. It feeds mostly on mice and voles, but never plays with them as pet cats do. It is now found only in Scotland and Europe although it once lived throughout Britain.

▲ **Norway lemming** 140mm; tail 17mm
This lemming is found in the high northern European mountains. It is a nocturnal, quarrelsome, small mammal. It feeds on grasses, and digs tunnels under the snow in winter to find food.

▲ **Pigmy shrew** 53mm; tail 38mm
It has a very thick, furry tail and tiny body. It eats small insects and spiders. Pigmy shrews are more common on moors and heaths than the larger common shrew.

▲ **Short-tailed field vole** 10cm; tail 38mm
Notice the small ears and eyes, blunt nose and short tail. It lives in rough grassland, often in large numbers. Smaller numbers are found on moors, marshes and bogs. There are none in Ireland.

▼ **Common lizard** up to 6·5cm; tail 8–12cm
The belly of the male turns orange or yellow in the breeding season. It is common on heaths, moors, bogs and grassland. In southern Europe it lives in damp places on mountains.

▲ **Sand lizard** 9cm; tail 11–15cm
The male has greenish sides. The female is grey or brown. It is rare in Britain, living only on some heaths and sand-dunes. In Europe it is found in mountains and grassland.

▼ **Stoat** 27cm; tail 11cm
This mammal is larger than a
weasel, and has a black tip to its
tail. It lives throughout most of
Britain in all habitats, including
heaths, moors and mountains.
Stoats feed mainly on rabbits,
birds, voles and mice.

▲ **Wild goat** 100–120cm
The goats found in the British
hills are domestic animals which
escaped over 100 years ago. They
are small and shaggy, and can
be white, black, brown or grey.
They mostly live on rocky
hillsides and moors.

▲ **Adder, viper** up to 65cm
(including tail)
The male is often paler, with a
darker pattern than the larger
female. It lives on heaths, moors
and bogs, and on mountains in
southern Europe. It eats small
animals, and is poisonous.

▲ **Smooth snake** up to 60cm
(including tail)
A rare snake in Britain, found
on a few heaths. In southern
Europe it lives in mountains,
open woods and hedgerows. It is
diurnal, and feeds mostly on
lizards. Not poisonous.

▲ **Natterjack toad** 7–8cm;
female larger than male.
The natterjack is rare in
Britain, and is only found on
heaths and sand-dunes with
ponds. It is more common in the
rest of Europe. Notice the bright
yellow stripe on its back.

Animal droppings

**Droppings show where the
animals have been.**

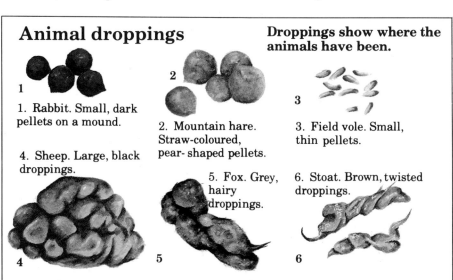

1. Rabbit. Small, dark
pellets on a mound.

2. Mountain hare.
Straw-coloured,
pear-shaped pellets.

3. Field vole. Small,
thin pellets.

4. Sheep. Large, black
droppings.

5. Fox. Grey,
hairy
droppings.

6. Stoat. Brown, twisted
droppings.

A bog

The peat in peat bogs is often very deep, up to 6 or 10 metres. It is usually full of water, and contains very little air. Plant roots have to breathe, so many plants have large air spaces in the stems to take oxygen from the air down to the roots. Some animals live in the oxygen zone round the plant roots. Neither the roots nor the animals can live very far down into the peat. The plants and animals which live here have to be well adapted to the wet, acid, airless conditions.

Plants and animals

Lousewort (21) and cross-leaved heath are common on the damp peat, with bog myrtle (8) and bog asphodel (19). Golden plovers (7) and dunlin (1) visit the bogs to nest. They feed on the fly, midge and cranefly larvae (25). Lizards (28) also live here and catch flies.

Tiny animals

Peat is not a rich habitat, like woodland soil, but many small animals live in it. Midge and cranefly larvae (25) feed on plant roots. Where there is more water, damselflies (6) lay their eggs, and water boatmen (5) feed on dead plant leaves and tiny algae.

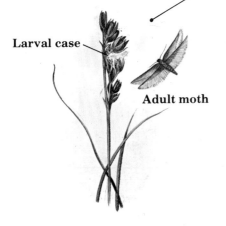

Larval case

Adult moth

◀ Case moth

This tiny moth lays its eggs on the heath rush (27). The caterpillar bores into the leaf but soon emerges and spins a case of silk. These pale cases can be found attached to the rush's fruits. Inside its case the larva is protected from predators, such as birds, and feeds on the fruits.

The **dead tree-stumps** show that trees once grew here. About 7,000 years ago it became very wet. The trees died and bogmosses increased. They did not decay in the wet, acid bogs, but became peat. The pale bands of unrotted peat developed in wet periods, while the partly-decayed, dark bands were formed at drier times.

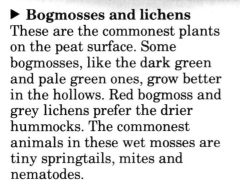

Key

1 Dunlin	9 Cloudberry	19 Bog asphodel
2 Black-headed gull	10 Large heath butterfly	20 Treepstump
3 Meadow pipit	11 White-beaked sedge	21 Lousewort
4 Cottongrass	12 Heather	22 Cranefly
5 Water boatman	13 Lichens	23 Midges
6 Damselflies	14 Butterwort	24 Deer sedge
7 Golden plover	15 Sundew	25 Midge larvae
8 Bog myrtle	16 Manchester treble bar moth	26 Silk case moth
	17 Cranberry	27 Heath rush
	18 Purple moor grass	28 Common lizard
		29 Bogmoss

Summer visitors

Colonies of gulls like these black-headed gulls (2) often nest on peat bogs. They choose a pile of dried plants, just out of reach of their neighbours. Here there is safety in numbers from predators like foxes. Gulls return to coasts, reservoirs and towns in the winter, when there is not much to eat near the peat bog.

▲ Butterwort

This is an insectivorous plant. It catches small flies on its sticky leaves, which roll in at the edges. It grows beside springs, on wet rocks, and by peaty pools.

▶ Bogmosses and lichens

These are the commonest plants on the peat surface. Some bogmosses, like the dark green and pale green ones, grow better in the hollows. Red bogmoss and grey lichens prefer the drier hummocks. The commonest animals in these wet mosses are tiny springtails, mites and nematodes.

Nematode   Springtail   Mite

151

Non-flowering plants

These plants produce spores instead of seeds. They include mosses and liverworts, ferns and fungi. Each produces its spores on a different part of the plant.

* Not to scale. Average height given.

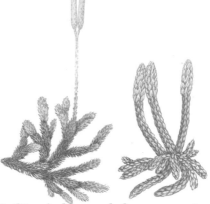

One stem

▲ **Bogmoss** 10–15cm
Different kinds of bogmoss can be seen as green, red or brownish patches in wet, peaty areas. Bogmosses hold large quantities of water. Doctors used them in the First World War to soak up blood.

▲ **Hair moss** 10–20cm
Small carpets of this dark green moss grow beside upland streams and bogs. The spore-capsule looks like a small box. When young it is covered with a hairy cap. Later this falls off, and the spores catapult out.

▲ **Stag's horn clubmoss** up to 15cm (left) **Alpine clubmoss** up to 6cm (right)
Most of the stems of stag's horn clubmoss creep along the ground, but those with spores are upright. Alpine clubmoss has short, upright stems. Both clubmosses grow in upland areas.

▲ **Woolly hair-moss** 12–15cm
This greyish-green moss has silvery hair points at the ends of the leaves. It spreads in soft, thick carpets over stony mountain tops. The small egg-shaped capsule is not often found.

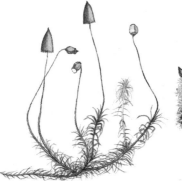

▲ **Lemon-scented fern** 30–100cm
The tall fronds with stubby lower leaflets grow in a rosette, and smell of lemon. Spores are clustered underneath the leaflet margins. It grows on screes, and by streams in hilly areas.

▲ **Hard fern** 10–40cm
The brittle fronds grow in a rosette on dry grassy or heathery banks. Spores are produced inside narrow, rolled leaflets on separate upright fronds. This fern is never found on limey soils.

▲ **Bracken** 30–180cm
The frond is divided into small leaflets, which form a triangular shape. Each frond grows singly from an underground stem. These stems cover large areas on hillsides and heaths. Bracken is poisonous.

▲ **Moonwort** 5–15cm
A small fern, with a single frond divided into 4 to 7 fan-shaped leaflets. The spores grow on a short branched stem, which is taller than the frond. Moonwort grows in summer on limestone and mountain grasslands.

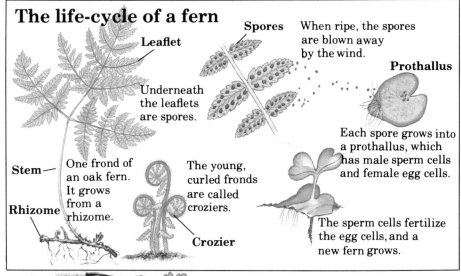

The life-cycle of a fern

Leaflet

Underneath the leaflets are spores.

Stem — One frond of an oak fern. It grows from a rhizome.

Rhizome

The young, curled fronds are called croziers.

Crozier

Spores — When ripe, the spores are blown away by the wind.

Prothallus

Each spore grows into a prothallus, which has male sperm cells and female egg cells.

The sperm cells fertilize the egg cells, and a new fern grows.

▲ **Hypnum cuppressiforme**
a moss
This is a common moss of heaths, moors, grassland and mountain ledges. It grows flat on the ground or on rocks, or spreads among the bases of heather stems. The curved leaves overlap neatly.

▲ **Wall rue** 3–12cm
The dull, dark green fronds form a small rosette on walls and rocks, especially on limestone. The spores are produced in long, thin clusters on the lower surface of the divided leaflets.

▲ **Cladonia coccifera** 2–4cm: a lichen
Most lichens are shades of grey, orange or yellow. This one is common on heaths and moors. It produces spores in the red tips of the short stalks, and larger, powdery grains on the outside of the stalks. Both blow away to form new plants.

▲ **Hypholoma elongatum**
5–9cm: a fungus
This is one of the few fungi which grow with bogmosses. The cap is pale yellow and shiny. The stalk is very slender. The brown gills under the cap produce spores.

▲ **Dung roundhead (Stropharia semiglobata)** 1–4cm
The caps are small, sticky and straw-coloured. This fungus usually grows on dung, such as grouse droppings. It feeds on the dung and helps it to rot.

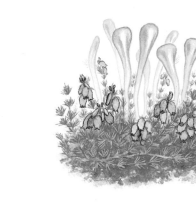

▲ **Clavaria argillacea** 3–8cm: a fungus
This is club-shaped, and can be dirty white or yellow. The spores are produced on the outside of the 'club'. It grows on peaty ground amongst heather and mosses.

Grasslands

The sheep are responsible for the grasslands here. They prevent shrubs and trees from spreading. The ungrazed rock ledges show what would happen if there were no sheep. The grassland on the left developed on acid soils. The plants and some of the animals are different from those on the limestone grassland on the right. In the middle is an old hay meadow on a limey soil. It is not grazed, so different plants grow here.

Acid grasslands
Not many different plants can grow here. Yellow tormentil and white heath bedstraw are common. Mat grass (19) covers much of the slope. Its wiry leaves are bleached by the sun. They are not very tasty, so sheep prefer the softer wavy hair grass (30). In wetter patches a curlew (8) nests in the soft rushes (9).

▼ Lesser bloody-nosed beetle
This is a small, rounded, shiny black beetle, which produces a deep red, blood-like liquid from its mouth and joints when disturbed. The bright colour warns off attackers. It crawls slowly over the plant leaves on which it feeds.

Heath bedstraw

Tormentil

Plants
The limestone rocks are covered with mosses and lichens, and tiny ferns like wall rue (24) cling to the sheltered crevices. Thyme and yellow kidney vetch (28) grow where there is more soil. There are many different flowers. Salad burnet (39) has male and female flowers on the same head. Pignut (26) has edible underground tubers.

Where there is no soil, the edges of the limestone blocks are dissolved away by rainwater. The gaps (grykes) and blocks (clints) form a 'limestone pavement'. Woodland plants, like dog's mercury (14) and lily of the valley (17), fill the grykes because they are damp and shady.

▶ Flowers and tiny animals
The purple flowers of the knapweed stand out in the mass of plants. The nectar attracts butterflies, hoverflies and bumblebees. Froghoppers and plant bugs suck the sugary sap.

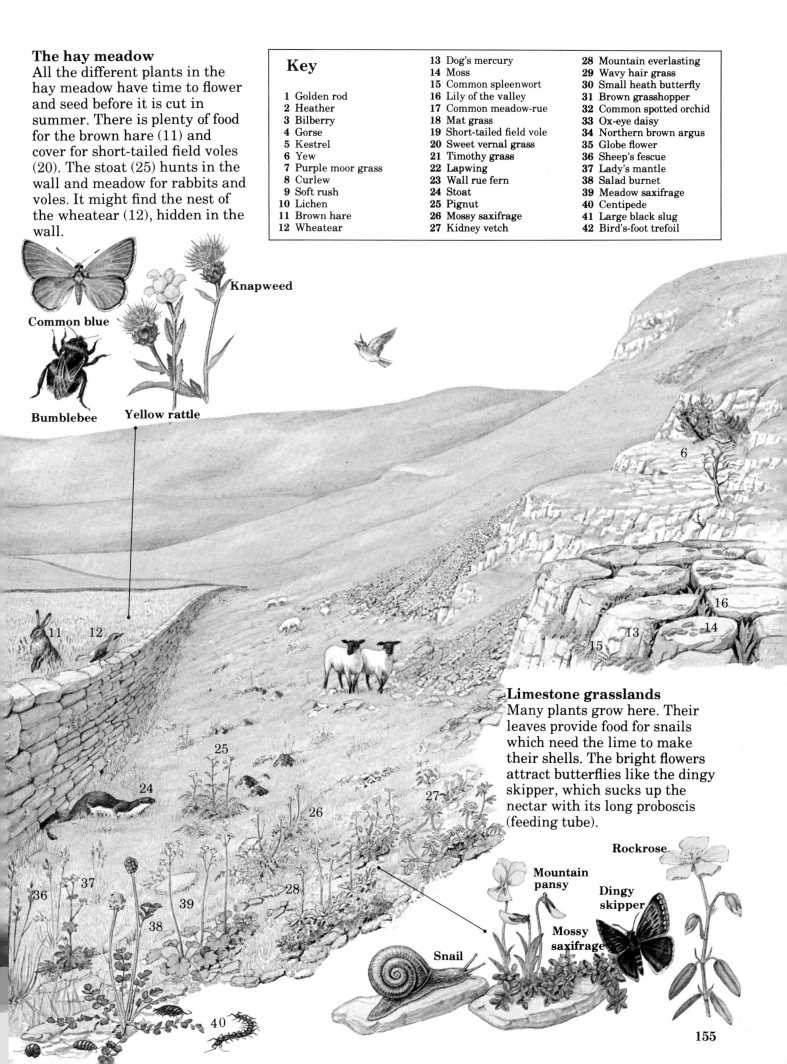

The hay meadow

All the different plants in the hay meadow have time to flower and seed before it is cut in summer. There is plenty of food for the brown hare (11) and cover for short-tailed field voles (20). The stoat (25) hunts in the wall and meadow for rabbits and voles. It might find the nest of the wheatear (12), hidden in the wall.

Key

1 Golden rod
2 Heather
3 Bilberry
4 Gorse
5 Kestrel
6 Yew
7 Purple moor grass
8 Curlew
9 Soft rush
10 Lichen
11 Brown hare
12 Wheatear
13 Dog's mercury
14 Moss
15 Common spleenwort
16 Lily of the valley
17 Common meadow-rue
18 Mat grass
19 Short-tailed field vole
20 Sweet vernal grass
21 Timothy grass
22 Lapwing
23 Wall rue fern
24 Stoat
25 Pignut
26 Mossy saxifrage
27 Kidney vetch
28 Mountain everlasting
29 Wavy hair grass
30 Small heath butterfly
31 Brown grasshopper
32 Common spotted orchid
33 Ox-eye daisy
34 Northern brown argus
35 Globe flower
36 Sheep's fescue
37 Lady's mantle
38 Salad burnet
39 Meadow saxifrage
40 Centipede
41 Large black slug
42 Bird's-foot trefoil

Knapweed

Common blue

Bumblebee

Yellow rattle

Limestone grasslands

Many plants grow here. Their leaves provide food for snails which need the lime to make their shells. The bright flowers attract butterflies like the dingy skipper, which sucks up the nectar with its long proboscis (feeding tube).

Rockrose

Mountain pansy

Dingy skipper

Mossy saxifrage

Snail

Tiny animals

Tiny animals without backbones are called 'invertebrates'. There are thousands of different types. Insects are one type. They have 6 jointed legs and a hard outer body covering. Beetles, bees and flies are all insects. Spiders and mites have 8 legs, and are another type of invertebrate.

* Not to scale. Average body-length given.

◀ **Wolf spider** 7–14mm **Orb-web spider** 15mm (above)
The wolf spider does not build a web. It hunts for insects on the ground at night. It lives in dry heaths and grasslands. It has shorter legs and is not as fast as other similar spiders.

This web spider spins a silken tent to hide in, and catches its prey in a web. It lives on heaths and rough grassland.

▲ **Froghopper** 11mm
These are the animals which jump when touched. The black and red colouring of this froghopper warns predators away. It sucks the juices from plant stems on grasslands. Its larvae live on plant roots.

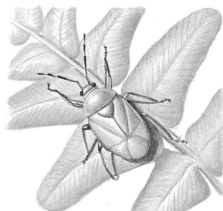

▲ **Bracken bug** 2·5–3mm
This small plant bug is pale brown. It hibernates in winter and feeds on fern spores in summer. It is found on bracken and other ferns in July and August on hills and heaths.

▲ **Soldier beetle** 8mm
This is a common beetle of grasslands and hedgerows, particularly on flowers like cow-parsley and hogweed. The adult and larvae do not feed on the flowers but on other insects.

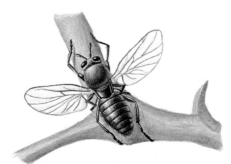

▲ **Black-fly** 2mm
This tiny fly has a stout body, with broad wings and thick legs. The female sucks blood and leaves an itchy spot. Swarms of black-fly can be seen in summer in moorlands and mountains.

▲ **Banded snail** 20mm shell width
The colour and number of bands may vary. The lip of the glossy shell is usually brown. It is common on lime-rich grassland and feeds on plants.

156

▲ **Hoverfly** 24mm
Its stripes make predators think this is a wasp, and avoid it. It does not sting. It hovers over flowers, and feeds on nectar. The larvae live in bogs. They have a long breathing tube to get oxygen from the surface.

▲ **Heath bumblebee** 14mm (male smaller)
Heath bumblebees collect pollen from heather and bilberry on heaths and moors. The pollen is stored in 'baskets' on the back legs and used to feed the larvae. Several bees use the same nest.

▲ **Upland ground beetle** 8mm
Ground beetles come out from under stones at night-time. Both the adults and the larvae run around, hunting for worms, slugs and small insects to eat. This ground beetle is common on moors and mountains.

▲ **Digger wasp** 14mm
The adults emerge from hibernation and mate. The female finds a spider and paralyses it with her sting. She drags it into her burrow, lays an egg in it and seals the burrow. The larva feeds on the spider, pupates in the winter and emerges as an adult the next summer.

▲ **Harvestman** 4–8mm
This is a common harvestman, found everywhere. It has 8 very long, jointed legs. Sometimes tiny, **red** parasitic mites attach themselves to its legs or body. It feeds on the remains of dead animals or plants.

▲ **Cranefly** 40mm; Ws 60mm
This is the largest British cranefly. It can only drink fluids, but the larvae feed on plant roots. They are called 'leatherjackets'. This large cranefly breeds in bogs. Other types live in grassy places.

The life-cycle of ants

Ants live in nests, each with a queen who lays the eggs, and many workers (wingless females, who do not breed). On one day in summer many winged males and females swarm and mate. The males die. The females find new nesting sites.

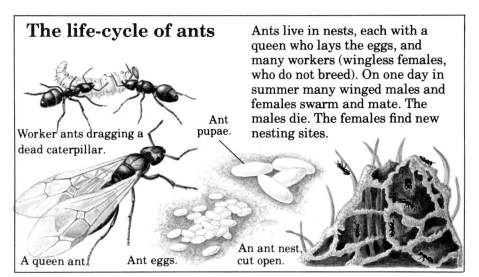

Worker ants dragging a dead caterpillar.

Ant pupae.

A queen ant.

Ant eggs.

An ant nest, cut open.

Using the land

Trees to heaths to trees again
In the Stone Age our heaths were oak forests. The people of the New Stone Age then started to cut down the trees. As the trees disappeared, the soils became more acid and infertile, because the tree roots were no longer bringing up lime and other minerals from deep in the soil. Heather, bilberry and broom like these poor soils, and spread to form heaths. Then they were used for grazing cattle and ponies. In winter strips of land were burnt to keep the plants young and more tasty.

Now few heaths are grazed, and trees are spreading. Scots pine, oak, gorse and silver birch are all common on heaths now.

Unfortunately, people set fire to many heaths, either accidentally or on purpose, in the summer. When it is dry and hot the plants burn fiercely, and animals are killed.

Many heaths have also been dug up for farming, quarries or roads. There are few left now, and some of the animals that live on heaths are becoming very rare. We are so worried about the natterjack toad, sand lizard and smooth snake, that they have been protected by an Act of Parliament. It is against the law to collect, injure or kill them.

Some heaths have been made into Nature Reserves. Here the plants and animals are safe, unless someone is stupid enough to drop a lighted match or cigarette on a dry day. So remember, if you start a fire and a heath is burnt, you could be destroying the habitat of many plants and animals *for ever*.

▲ This shows some of the dreadful effects of an accidental fire on a heath. The heather has been burnt away, and trees have been scorched. Slow-moving animals, insects, birds' eggs and chicks have all been destroyed. The heath may never recover.

The moors
Most moors, too, were once covered by trees. The forests gradually died out because of burning, which improved the plant growth for grazing animals, and because of the grazing itself. When the climate became wetter, peat began to develop in the hollows. This also prevented trees from growing.

The poor, wet, peaty soils were just right for the heather, bracken, bilberry and cottongrasses which cover the moors today.

As you have seen, trees manage to grow in sheltered moorland valleys on ledges where sheep cannot reach them. But it is not only grazing which prevents tree growth on the open moors. Winter burning is still very important. Shepherds burn moors occasionally to get fresh young plant growth for their sheep to eat, but heather burning is also necessary for grouse. Grouse feed on young heather, but nest in old, thick heather. Grouse set up their territories in November. The better the heather is for food and nesting, the smaller the territories will be. The smaller the territories, the more grouse a moor will hold. Since some people are willing to pay a great deal to be able to shoot grouse in the autumn, the moor owner wants to have as many grouse as possible.

To achieve this, the gamekeeper (someone who is rather like a shepherd for grouse instead of sheep) burns small, narrow strips of heather in winter. The result is a patchwork quilt of dark, old heather and pale, young plants. The heather is left to grow for about ten years before it is burnt again.

The burning is planned very carefully. Fire-breaks are cut so that the fire does not spread to a larger area. The fire is not big enough to burn the peat, so the hibernating animals are safe. The burnt area is so small that birds and mammals can get out of the way.

Heather recovers very well after a fire, which is why few other plants grow with it. The best places for flowers to grow on moorland are in the narrow valleys, which are seldom burnt.

Grasslands

Where grouse are not important, the farmer usually increases the number of sheep on a hillside. These eat the heather until it disappears and an acid grassland develops.

Limestone grassland has probably been grazed for thousands of years, and has never been moorland. It is full of masses of different flowers. Even this grassland was probably once covered by trees.

▲ **Peat erosion produces these deep groughs and steep haggs. Gradually the peat will disappear, leaving bare rock on which little can grow.**

The hills

Some hills are used for other purposes. Many are now covered with big plantations of conifer trees. The dense tree-cover shuts out light to the ground, so plants like heather and gorse disappear. Merlins, grouse and meadow pipits cannot live in these plantations, so they too disappear. Different birds come in to live there.

Reservoirs have been made in some moorland valleys. These destroy the valley-bottom habitats, but create new ones, often used by wintering gulls and ducks.

In some places people dig peat and burn it for cooking and heating.

Peat is disappearing from some hill tops for other reasons. This may be a natural process, caused by rain and wind removing peat. Or it may happen because repeated burning and grazing has helped to kill some of the plant cover, which leaves the ground open to wind and water erosion. Deep gullies (called groughs) and peat mounds (haggs) are the result. It is very easy to get lost in them.

◄ **In many areas peat is used for fuel. It is cut into large slabs using special tools, then stacked up to dry. When dry, peat burns very well.**

Acknowledgments

Graham Allen/Linden Artists 10–11, 16–17, 20–21, 26–27, 84–85, 88–89, 92–93
David Astin/Linden Artists 82, 83
Bob Bampton/The Garden Studio 138–139
Janet Blakeley/N E Middleton 132–133, 144–145, 152–153
Wendy Bramall/Artist Partners Ltd 56–57, 62–63, 68–69, 74–75, 80–81, 134–135, 150–151
Rhoda Burns/Drawing Attention 8–9, 12–13, 14–15, 18–19, 24–25, 28–29
Sally Burrough/N E Middleton 130–131
Sara De'Ath/Artist Partners Ltd 112–113
Jane Fern/The Garden Studio 128–129
Tim Hayward/Linden Artists 86–87, 98–99
Bob Hersey/Linden Artists 94–95, 106–107
Kristin Jakob/The Garden Studio 126–127
Felicity Kaye/The Garden Studio 120–121
Pat Lenander/Temple Art Group 6–7
Mick Loats/The Garden Studio 124–125
Vanessa Luff 32–33, 36–37, 44–45, 50–51, 118–119, 146–147

Alan Male/Linden Artists 102–103
Josephine Martin/The Garden Studio 108–109, 154–155
Tony Morris/Linda Rogers Associates 22–23
Robert Morton/Linden Artists 96–97, 100–101
David Nash 30
Margaret Nicholls 114–115
Cynthia Pow/N E Middleton Ltd 70–71, 78–79
Steve Rigby 34–35, 38–39, 40–41, 42–43, 46–47, 48–49, 52–53, 58–59, 60–61, 64–65, 66–67, 72–73, 76–77
John Rignall/Linden Artists 90–91, 104–105
Andrew Riley/The Garden Studio 116–117, 156–157
Ursula Seiger/N E Middleton 140–141
Neil Smith 31
Charlotte Snook 4–5
Derek Steele/John Martin & Artists Ltd 158–159
Mike Woodhatch/David Lewis Associates 122–123, 142–143

First published in Great Britain in six volumes:
Wildlife in Towns
Life in Ponds and Streams
Life on the Seashore
The Wildlife of Woodlands
The Wildlife of Farmland
The Wildlife of Mountains and Moorlands

Reprinted in 1989 as a single volume by Macdonald & Co (Publishers) Ltd under the Black Cat imprint. Reprinted 1990.

Simon & Schuster Young Books
Simon & Schuster Ltd
Wolsey House
Wolsey Road
Hemel Hempstead
Herts HP2 4SS

ISBN 0 7481 0154 3

Printed in Hong Kong